RECIPES FOR HEALTH

Anaemia

By the same author

RECIPES FOR HEALTH
Irritable Bowel Syndrome
(with Ann Page-Wood)

RECIPES FOR HEALTH
Premenstrual Syndrome

*Anaemia: A guide to causes,
treatment and prevention*

RECIPES FOR HEALTH

Anaemia

Over 100 recipes for overcoming iron-deficiency

JILL DAVIES

Thorsons
An Imprint of HarperCollinsPublishers

Thorsons
An Imprint of HarperCollins*Publishers*
77–85 Fulham Palace Road,
Hammersmith, London W6 8JB
1160 Battery Street,
San Francisco, California 94111–1213

Published by Thorsons 1995
1   3   5   7   9   10   8   6   4   2

A catalogue record for this book is
available from the British Library

ISBN 0 7225 2914 7

Typeset by Harper Phototypesetters Limited,
Northampton
Printed in Great Britain by
HarperCollinsManufacturing, Glasgow

Contents

1

What Is Anaemia?

A NAEMIA IS A major public health problem, and about 30 per cent of the population suffer from the condition.

WHAT ARE THE SYMPTOMS OF ANAEMIA?

If you are anaemic you are likely to have some, if not all, of the following symptoms:

- Tiredness and weakness
- Lethargy
- Headaches
- Dizziness, shortness of breath and palpitations (rapid heart action) brought on by exertion
- Pale complexion described as pallor

Other symptoms may be present depending on the cause of your anaemia. For example, if lack of iron is the problem, your nails may be brittle. The characteristic symptoms of anaemia develop because of lack of oxygen in the body tissues. This is not due to lack of air being breathed in, but to problems associated with the red blood cells, the *erythrocytes*, that are found in blood.

WHAT CAUSES ANAEMIA?

To understand how anaemia develops it is necessary to know about the red blood cells. These cells are produced in the bone marrow and the sequence of events is shown in Figure 1.1. Red blood cells are amongst the smallest cells in the body – about 7 micrometres in diameter – and are the most numerous type of cell present in blood. In one cubic millimetre of blood there are about 5 million red blood cells. The cells are disc-shaped, soft and flexible and red in colour. The typical red colour is due the presence of the blood pigment called *haemoglobin* which consists of the following: *Iron* and *protein* – haem refers to the iron part and globin to the protein.

The characteristic features of the red cells are important with regard to their function in carrying oxygen to the body tissues. The disc-shape ensures that each cell has a large surface area which enables them to take up oxygen efficiently when the blood reaches the lungs. The softness and flexibility of the red cells allows them to squeeze through the tiny blood vessels (capillaries) so that the oxygen can be conveyed to the cells of the body. If you are in good health the amount of haemoglobin in your blood is stable and maintained by a strict balance (see Table 1.1). If haemoglobin levels fall the oxygen-

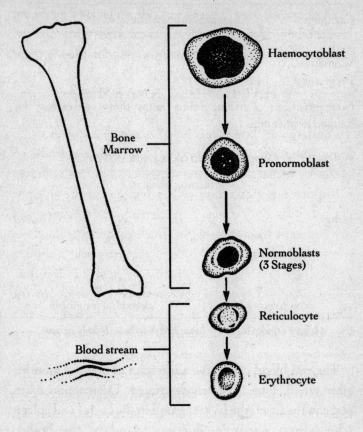

Bone Marrow

Blood stream

Haemocytoblast

Pronormoblast

Normoblasts
(3 Stages)

Reticulocyte

Erythrocyte

Figure 1.1 Red blood cell production

carrying capacity of the blood is reduced. Figure 1.2
shows the principles involved in the transfer of oxygen
from breathing, up until it is taken up by the body cells.

TABLE 1.1 HAEMOGLOBIN LEVELS

Category	g of haemoglobin per litre of blood
Men	130
Women	120
Pregnancy	110

Concentrations of haemoglobin below these values may be defined as anaemia.

FIGURE 1.2 HAEMOGLOBIN AND OXYGEN TRANSFER

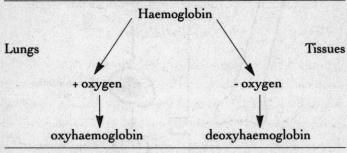

Oxygen is picked up in the lungs and distributed to body tissues.

The red blood cells have a life span of about 4 months, after which time they are destroyed. Destruction takes place in the liver (the largest gland in the body) and spleen (the largest endocrine/ductless gland in the body). However, the story does not end here. Despite the ageing and death of the red blood cells the iron in the haemoglobin is not wasted. The iron is saved and used over and over again to produce new red blood cells.

Anaemia may occur for a variety of reasons, but the most common one is lack of iron. Deficiency of certain vitamins, particularly folate and vitamin B_{12}, can also lead to anaemia. Several other nutrients have a role in the life of the red blood cell and may be implicated in anaemia; for example vitamins B_2, B_6, C and E, copper and protein. Nutrition is not the only factor; anaemia can result from radiotherapy, anti-cancer drugs and certain types of viral infection. Some people may be anaemic due to genetic reasons as in the case of sickle cell anaemia, and others may develop the condition as a consequence of malaria or failure of the immune system as in the case of AIDS.

This book focuses on anaemias of nutritional origin.

Iron-deficiency

In iron-deficiency anaemia the red blood cells are smaller than usual and hence the term microcytic is used. The cells are paler in colour because they do not contain their full complement of haemoglobin and are described as hypochromic (see Figure 1.3). This type of anaemia develops if there is not enough iron available for the production of haemoglobin. Lack of iron for the production of haemoglobin may be caused by:

- Loss of iron from the body due to blood loss
- Poor absorption of iron from the diet
- Lack of iron in the diet

The main cause of iron-deficiency is loss of iron as a result of losing blood. Blood losses of iron may occur for a number of reasons. If you are female and have particularly heavy periods you may be vulnerable to iron-deficiency anaemia. Most women lose about 44 millilitres of blood per cycle but some may lose considerably more. Blood loss

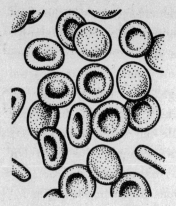

- Red blood cells about 7 micrometres in diameter

- Red colour

- Full complement of haemoglobin

- Red blood cells smaller

- Paler in colour

- Reduced haemoglobin level

Figure 1.3 Red blood cells in a healthy person and in iron-deficiency anaemia

occurs when babies are born, in the afterbirth. Any major surgical operations or blood loss due to an injury can lead to loss of body iron. Certain disorders of health such as bleeding gums, haemorrhoids and cancer of the stomach can lead to loss of blood. Prolonged treatment with certain drugs may cause gastrointestinal bleeding. If you donate blood you obviously lower your own body's content of iron and it is advisable to allow 6-month intervals between donations for iron stores to be replenished.

The second most common cause of iron-deficiency is poor absorption of iron from the diet. This may be associated with certain conditions including, for example, coeliac disease (where the lining of the small intestine is damaged by gluten, the protein derived from wheat and other cereals).

The third cause of iron-deficiency is a diet that does not provide enough iron. Old people living alone with lack of interest in food are particularly vulnerable. Children, adolescents and pregnant women may not have enough iron in their diets to meet the demands of growth and the heavy demands of pregnancy. If you are attempting to slim, low food intakes may result in low intakes of iron.

Folate-deficiency

Anaemia due to folate-deficiency is characterized by red blood cells that are larger than normal and hence the term macrocytic is applied. The red blood cells are also deformed; their rate of production is decreased and so is their lifespan.

Folate is needed for the orderly production of deoxyribonucleic acid (DNA) in all tissue cells. In bone marrow it is required for the normal production of red blood cells. Folate-deficiency is usually due to low dietary intakes.

Elderly people who live on their own are at particular risk of folate-deficiency. Low intakes may arise from factors such as lack of interest in food, poverty and immobility. Ill-fitting dentures may inhibit the consumption of food or result in the tendency to overcook green vegetables which will destroy folate. Approximately 8 per cent of people over the age of 65 in Britain have low levels of folate in their blood.

Folate-deficiency is common in tropical areas where the diet is poor due to poverty. In this case infants, young children and pregnant women are particularly vulnerable.

Excessive intakes of alcohol have been associated with folate-deficiency.

It may also be caused by problems of absorption of the vitamin from the small intestine. This could arise from the administration of certain drugs and from health disorders impairing absorption such as *coeliac disease*.

Vitamin B₁₂-deficiency

Like folate, vitamin B_{12} is necessary for the production of DNA and the normal development of red blood cells. Lack of vitamin B_{12} affects the red blood cells in the same way as deficiency of folate. Vitamin B_{12}-deficiency rarely results from low intakes and is more generally associated with poor absorption of the vitamin from the small intestine.

Vitamin B_{12}-deficiency is a possible risk for vegans (strict vegetarians) because this particular vitamin is not naturally present in foods of plant origin. Vegetarianism is becoming increasingly popular especially amongst young people and if this progresses to veganism it is important to seek dietary advice from either the Vegetarian or Vegan Societies.

A deficiency may also result from lack of intrinsic factor which is normally produced by cells found in the lining of the stomach. Intrinsic factor is necessary for the absorption of vitamin B_{12}. Failure to produce this factor means that no matter how much vitamin B_{12} is present (from food or supplements), it cannot be absorbed from the digestive tract. Anaemia caused in this way is called *pernicious anaemia*. This disorder tends to run in families, to start in middle age and to affect women more than men.

Poor absorption of vitamin B_{12} may be caused by certain conditions, for example, *Crohn's disease* (an inflammatory lesion of the intestines of unknown cause). In Finland some people develop B_{12}-deficiency anaemia as a consequence of having tapeworm *Diphyllobothrium latum* in their gut. The worm is widespread in fish and about 2 per cent of the Finnish population carry it. The tapeworm absorbs the vitamin so there is little, if any, left for the human host!

Pregnancy

Women who are pregnant may be vulnerable to anaemia associated with the demands for folate and iron. Both nutrients are essential for red cell production and during pregnancy there is an increase in the production of the red blood cells. If the pregnant woman is enjoying good health and is well nourished supplements will not be prescribed.

Folic acid supplements are sometimes prescribed as indeed are iron supplements. If you have any queries about taking supplements during pregnancy the best person to ask is your doctor.

Pregnant women need to be very careful about food choice. Some foods which are rich in iron and folic acid may actually be harmful. Liver, for example, contains very high amounts of vitamin A which can be harmful to the developing fetus during the first trimester (first 3 months) of pregnancy. The Department of Health advises pregnant women not to eat liver, or products derived from liver such as liver pâté and liver sausage.

HOW IS ANAEMIA DIAGNOSED?

If you suspect that you are anaemic it is very important that you seek the advice of your doctor. *On no account attempt self-diagnosis.* You can help your doctor enormously by giving an accurate account of any symptoms you have experienced and by taking along any medication you might be taking. If you have changed your diet in any way or are aware of blood loss it is important to bring this to your doctor's notice. Apart from this background information it may be necessary for a sample of blood to be taken and various tests carried out:

- *Measurement of haemoglobin* – if your concentration of haemoglobin is below a set value you will be diagnosed as anaemic (see Table 1.1)
- *Examination of blood film* – under the microscope the red cells will be clearly visible and changes in shape, size and colour seen
- *Other tests* – such as a bone marrow biopsy (removal of a small sample of marrow for analysis) will show if the bone marrow is producing large deformed red cells. If *pernicious anaemia* is suspected you may be asked to do a special test to find out if your problem is due to lack of the intrinsic factor.

2

What to Do if You Are Anaemic

I F YOU HAVE been diagnosed as anaemic you may be advised to make some changes to your *diet* or to take *supplements* or you may be given a course of *injections*. Clearly any treatment prescribed will depend upon the underlying cause of the condition and any other relevant information in your medical history.

SUPPLEMENTS (ORAL ADMINISTRATION)

Table 2.1 gives some examples of nutritional supplements that may be prescribed for treating anaemia. Supplements come in a variety of different forms including *tablets*, *capsules*, *liquids*, *syrups* and *elixirs*.

When supplements are prescribed it is important to keep to the following guidelines:

- Follow the instructions on the label
- Drink a glass of cold water immediately afterwards
- Keep a note of any side effects and tell your doctor

without delay
- If your teeth become discoloured (this may happen with liquid iron preparations) try drinking the preparation through a straw
- Complete the full course of treatment unless advised otherwise by your doctor.

TABLE 2.1 SUPPLEMENTS FOR TREATING ANAEMIA*

Oral preparation	Tablet (✓)	Capsule (✓)	Liquid (✓)	Syrup (✓)	Elixir (✓)
Iron					
(Ferrous Sulphate)					
Feospan		✓			
(Ferrous Fumarate)					
Fersaday	✓				
(Ferrous Glycine Sulphate)					
Plesmet				✓	
(Ferrous Succinate)					
Ferromyn					✓
Folate					
(Folic Acid)					
Folic Acid Tablets	✓				
Lexpec				✓ (sugar free)	
Vitamin B$_{12}$					
(Cyanocobalamin)					
Cytacon	✓				

*Information taken from the *British National Formulary*.

Side-effects are particularly associated with iron preparations and these may include any of the following:

- Gastrointestinal irritation
- Abdominal pain
- Nausea
- Vomiting
- Diarrhoea
- Constipation
- Blackened faeces
- Blackened teeth (liquid preparations)

INJECTIONS
(PARENTERAL ADMINISTRATION)

If you have been diagnosed as having *pernicious anaemia*, whereby vitamin B_{12} cannot be absorbed from your digestive tract, you will probably be advised to have injections of the vitamin for the rest of your life.

In some circumstances you may be advised to administer iron by injection. This would be likely if you had any of the following:

- Difficulty in taking oral iron
- Severe gastrointestinal side-effects
- Continued loss of blood, eg due to an ulcer
- Malabsorption of iron, eg after surgical removal of all or part of the stomach

Depending on the nature of the preparation to be

administered, the injection would be given through the skin and underlying fatty tissue into either a muscle or vein. The former is described as an *intramuscular injection* and the latter as an *intravenous injection*.

Examples of preparations administered in this way are given in Table 2.2. As in the case of oral preparations any side-effects should be reported to your doctor, and any specific guidelines adhered to.

TABLE 2.2 INJECTIONS FOR TREATING ANAEMIA*

Parenteral preparations	Intramuscular (✓)	Intravenous (✓)
Vitamin B$_{12}$ (Hydroxycobalamin) Cobalin-H	✓	
(Cyanocobalamin) Cytamen	✓	
Iron (Iron Sorbitol) Jectofer	✓	

*Information taken from the *British National Formulary*.

DIET

Changes to your diet may be suggested and foods rich in the 'problem' nutrients prescribed. This may sound quite straightforward but such advice needs careful interpretation.

For anaemia resulting from *iron-deficiency* certain foods known to be rich sources of iron (see Table 2.3) may be recommended. Offal would not be acceptable to vegetarians. Curry powder appears to have the highest content of iron of all the foods listed but the amount that would be in a food portion would be much smaller than 100 grams! Black treacle has a reasonable amount of iron in it, but what about all the sugar? Drinks of red wine yield iron, but are alcoholic beverages the best way of getting iron into your body? Chocoholics will no doubt be interested that chocolate can add to the iron content of diet.

TABLE 2.3 RICH SOURCES OF IRON

Food	*mg of iron per 100 g of food*
Curry powder	58.3
Liver, raw, pig	21.0
lamb	9.4
calf	8.0
Cocoa powder	10.5
Black treacle	9.2
Chocolate, plain	2.4
Red wine	0.9

If your anaemia is due to lack of *folate*, foods rich in this vitamin such as *green leafy vegetables*, *liver* and *yeast extract* may be recommended. Again, liver may not always be acceptable, and although yeast extract contains 1010 micrograms of folate per 100 grams, the size of a food portion is about 4 grams and it has a high salt content. Choosing green leafy vegetables is a good idea as long as the vegetables are not subjected to prolonged cooking which will destroy the vitamin.

To increase the *vitamin B_{12}* content of the diet of vegetarians, particularly vegans, foods listed in Table 2.4 may be suggested. The vitamin is found in these foods either as a result of bacterial contamination, as in the case of fermented foods and sea vegetables, or it is added to the food. Examples of these fortified foods include certain brands of soya milk, margarines and yeast extracts.

TABLE 2.4 SOURCES OF VITAMIN B$_{12}$ SUITABLE FOR VEGANS

Food	μg of vitamin B$_{12}$ per 100 g of food
Fortified products*	
yeast extract	50.0
margarine	5.0
soya milk, diluted	1.6
Sea vegetables, dried, raw	
nori	27.5
kombu	2.8
wakame	2.5
Fermented foods	
miso, bean paste	0.2
tempeh, soya bean cake	0.1 (may be as high as 1.6 μg with bacterial contamination)

*Read food labels to identify these specially fortified foods.

3

The Dietary Approach

TO REDUCE THE risk of developing nutritional deficiencies that could lead to anaemia or as part of the treatment aimed at curing the condition it is helpful to know more about iron, folate and vitamin B_{12}. Perhaps the first logical question is how much of these nutrients do we need?

DIETARY REFERENCE VALUES (DRVs)

In Britain the most recently published figures for nutritional intakes are found in the Department of Health's report called *Dietary Reference Values for Food Energy and Nutrients for the United Kingdom*. The report gives a range of values, including Reference Nutrient Intakes (RNI), which are relevant to the prevention and treatment of anaemias of nutritional origin.

The RNI is defined as the amount of a nutrient that is enough for almost everyone, even a person who has high needs for the nutrient. The level of intake is much higher than most people need. If you consume the RNI of a nutrient you are most unlikely to be deficient in that nutrient. Table 3.1 shows the RNIs for iron, folate and vitamin B_{12}.

TABLE 3.1 REFERENCE NUTRIENT INTAKES* (RNIs) FOR IRON, FOLATE AND VITAMIN B_{12}

Sex	Age (yrs)	Iron (mg/d)	Folate (μg/d)	Vitamin B_{12} (μg/d)
Males, females	1–3	6.9	70	0.5
	4–6	6.1	100	0.8
	7–10	8.7	150	1.0
Males	11–14	11.3	200	1.2
	15–18	11.3	200	1.5
	19–50	8.7	200	1.5
	50+	8.7	200	1.5
Females	11–14	14.8**	200	1.2
	15–18	14.8**	200	1.5
	19–50	14.8**	200	1.5
	50+	8.7	200	1.5
Pregnancy		–	+100	–
Lactation		–	+ 60	+0.5

* Taken from *Dietary Reference Values for Food Energy and Nutrients for the United Kingdom*.
** Women with high menstrual losses may be advised to take iron supplements.

RECOMMENDED DIETARY ALLOWANCES (RDAs)

In the United States of America the latest figures for nutrient intakes are given in the National Research Council's book *Recommended Dietary Allowances*. The RDAs are the levels of intake of essential nutrients that, on the basis of scientific knowledge, are judged by the Food and Nutrition Board (the panel that had responsibility for the figures) to be adequate to meet the known nutrient needs of practically all healthy people. Table 3.2 shows the RDAs for iron, folate and vitamin B_{12}.

WHICH FOODS TO CHOOSE

To increase your intakes of iron, folate or B_{12} it is useful to know about the amount of these nutrients likely to be found in food portions. Table 3.3 shows a selection of foods providing different amounts of iron, folate and vitamin B_{12}.

Iron is widely distributed in foods and this is clearly shown in Table 3.3. About two-thirds of iron in the diet comes from vegetable sources and many foods provide iron in useful amounts. If you are moving towards a vegetarian or vegan diet you can easily get your 'iron rations' and will be no more at risk of iron-deficiency anaemia than others. There is, however, one very important proviso: you need to eat a varied diet to ensure efficient absorption of iron. Dietary Reference Values and

Recommended Dietary Allowances assume a mixed diet in this respect.

TABLE 3.2 RECOMMENDED DIETARY ALLOWANCES* (RDAS) FOR IRON, FOLATE AND VITAMIN B_{12}

Sex	Age (yrs)	Iron (mg/∂)	Folate (µg/∂)	Vitamin B_{12} (µg/∂)
Males, females	1–3	10	50	0.7
	4–6	10	75	1.0
	7–10	10	100	1.4
Males	11–14	12	150	2.0
	15–18	12	200	2.0
	19–50	10	200	2.0
	50+	10	200	2.0
Females	11–14	15	150	2.0
	15–18	15	180	2.0
	19–50	15	180	2.0
	50+	10	180	2.0
Pregnancy		30	400	2.2
Lactation				
1st 6 months		15	280	2.6
2nd 6 months			260	2.6

* Taken from *Recommended Dietary Allowances* designed for the maintenance of good nutrition of practically all healthy people in the United States.

TABLE 3.3 THE AMOUNT OF IRON, FOLATE AND VITAMIN B_{12} IN STANDARD FOOD PORTIONS*

Food	Size of portion	Weight (g)	Iron (mg)	Folate (μg)	Vitamin B_{12} (μg)
PROTEIN-RICH DISHES					
Cheese					
Cheddar	1 slice	40	0.1	13	0.4
Cottage cheese	1 serving	45	0	12	0.3
Feta cheese	1 slice	40	0.1	9	0.4
Eggs (chickens)					
Boiled	1 (size 2)	60	1.0	21	0.6
Scrambled with milk	2 eggs	140	2.2	39	2.9
Fish					
Cod, steaks, grilled	2 steaks	130	0.5	13	2.6
Plaice, fillets, steamed	2 small fillets	120	0.7	13	2.4
Sardines, canned in tomato sauce	1 serving	85	3.9	11	11.9
Meat					
Beef steak, rump, lean, grilled	1 steak	155	5.4	26	3.1

Food	Size of portion	Weight (g)	Iron (mg)	Folate (μg)	Vitamin B$_{12}$ (μg)
Meat (continued)					
Lamb, chops, loin, grilled	2 chops	160	2.4	3	3.2
Pork, leg, roasted	1 serving	85	1.1	6	1.7
Offal					
Faggots	2 faggots	190	15.8	42	9.5
Liver, lambs, fried	1 serving	90	9.0	216	72.9
Liver pâté	1 serving	60	4.3	53	4.3
Poultry					
Chicken, meat and skin, roasted	1 serving	85	0.7	N	Tr
Duck, meat and skin, roasted	1 serving	85	2.3	N	1.7
Turkey, meat and skin, roasted	1 serving	85	0.8	N	N
Pulses and nuts					
Baked beans, canned in tomato sauce	1 serving	200	2.8	44	0
Cashew nuts	20 kernels	40	2.5	27	0
Tofu, soya bean, steamed	1 serving	60	0.7	9	0
Peanuts	32 kernels	30	0.8	33	0

Food	Size of portion	Weight (g)	Iron (mg)	Folate (µg)	Vitamin B₁₂ (µg)
FRUIT AND VEGETABLES					
Fruit					
Avocado pear	½ pear	130	0.5	14	0
Banana	1 banana	135	0.3	12	0
Currants	2 handfuls	35	0.5	1	0
Grapefruit	½ grapefruit	140	0.1	36	0
Orange	1 orange	245	0.2	54	0
Raspberries	15 raspberries	70	0.5	23	0
Vegetables					
Brussels sprouts, boiled	1 serving	115	0.6	127	0
Cabbage, boiled	1 serving	75	0.2	22	0
Carrots, young, boiled	1 serving	65	0.3	11	0
Cauliflower, boiled	1 serving	100	0.4	51	0
Peas, frozen, boiled	1 serving	75	1.2	35	0
Potatoes, old, boiled	1 serving	150	0.6	39	0

Food	Size of portion	Weight (g)	Iron (mg)	Folate (μg)	Vitamin B$_{12}$ (μg)
CEREALS					
Biscuits					
Oatcakes	2 oatcakes	26	1.2	7	0
Bread, from large loaf, medium sliced					
brown	2 slices	70	1.5	28	0
white	2 slices	75	1.2	22	0
wholemeal	2 slices	70	1.9	27	0
Breakfast cereals					
All-Bran	1 bowl	45	5.4	113	0.9
Grapenuts	1 bowl	90	8.6	315	4.5
Muesli, Swiss style	1 bowl	95	5.3	133	0
Rice and pasta					
Rice, brown, boiled	1 serving	165	0.8	17	0
white, boiled	1 serving	165	0.3	5	0
Pasta, white, boiled	1 serving	150	0.8	6	0
wholemeal, boiled	1 serving	150	2.1	11	0

*Food portion sizes derived from the *Nutrient Content of Food Portions* and nutritional values from The Royal Society of Chemistry/Ministry of Agriculture Fisheries and Food Tables of Food Composition.

Recommended Dietary Allowances assume a mixed diet in this respect.

Iron found in meat, described as *haem-iron*, is readily absorbed in the digestive tract. Iron found in plant foods and some animal products is called *non-haem iron* and is not well absorbed. To enhance absorption it is useful to eat foods rich in vitamin C or to eat meat which will provide certain amino acids that will convert the non-haem iron into an absorbable form. As well as this, non-haem iron is readily bound into an unavailable form by certain foods, such as tannin in tea.

Folate is present in a wide range of foods (see Table 3.3). Foods that are rich in B vitamins and vitamin C are generally rich in folate as well, and this points to sensible meal planning, ensuring that a mixture of foods is eaten. Both meat eaters and vegetarians have every chance of ensuring adequate intakes of folate. The main words of caution are not to overcook your vegetables: folate, as mentioned earlier, is readily destroyed by overcooking.

Vitamin B_{12} is found in foods of animal origin only. Therefore if you are eating a mixed diet based on foods of both plant and animal origin you shouldn't have a problem of low intake. If you are living on a diet of plant foods only, however, you will need to plan your meals a little more carefully, and Table 2.4 is a useful starting point. If you are a vegetarian who consumes plenty of pulse and nut dishes, but little milk, cheese or eggs or products derived from them you may be at risk of low vitamin B_{12} intake. In this situation you can either choose more dairy foods and eggs (see Table 3.3) or go for foods listed in Table 2.4 and seek specialist advice as for vegans.

The 'Right' Mix

The secret of success is not to focus narrowly on a particular nutrient but to consider the diet as a whole. By all means refer to figures in the tables as a guide but be sure to plan meals to include foods from the following groups:

- Protein rich (eg eggs, cheese, fish, meat, pulses and nuts)
- Vegetables and fruit
- Cereals, preferably unrefined

Table 3.3 was designed with this meal planning scheme in mind. Combining these foods will facilitate the efficient use of the nutrients in the body, as will eating a *breakfast*, *midday* and *evening meal*.

It is not intended that you tot up the amounts of the anaemia-associated nutrients. The figures are merely to act as a general guide. You may be interested in boosting your *iron* intake and the recipe key will be helpful in this respect. If *folate* is a problem the figures are a general guide. But do remember it is not possible to be precise about this nutrient as losses occur during the cooking of vegetables. If you are changing to a vegetarian diet with a predominance of plant-based foods you might like to consider the dishes with eggs and cheese so that you don't fall short of *vitamin B_{12}*.

Recipe Notes

- Follow either Metric or Imperial measures for the recipes in this book as they are not interchangeable
- All spoon measures are level, unless otherwise specified
- Size 2 eggs should be used
- Milk is semi-skimmed unless otherwise stated
- Plain flour is used unless otherwise stated

4

Breakfasts

BACON BANNOCK

Fe	Fol	B$_{12}$
2.9	41	0.46

Serves 4

Metric/Imperial		*American*
5 rashers	streaky bacon, rindless	5 slices
225g/8oz	wholemeal self-raising flour	2 cups
	freshly ground black pepper	
55g/2oz	margarine	1/4 cup
1	egg, beaten	1
140ml/1/4 pint	milk	2/3 cup

1. Grill the bacon until crisp, then finely chop.
2. Sift the flour and pepper into a mixing bowl and tip in any bran remaining in the sieve.
3. Add the margarine and rub into the flour until the mixture resembles fine breadcrumbs.
4. Stir in the bacon, egg and half the milk. Continue adding the milk until the ingredients hold together as a soft dough.

5. Turn the dough on to a lightly floured work surface, knead gently and shape into a 18cm/7 inch-round.
6. Mark the round into 8 sections. Place on a non-stick or lightly greased baking sheet.
7. Bake in a preheated oven at 230°C/450°F/gas mark 8 for about 20 minutes.
8. Serve hot, with freshly cooked scrambled eggs.

BLACK PUDDING SAUTÉ

Serves 4

Fe	Fol	B$_{12}$
12.0	52	0.56

Metric/Imperial		*American*
455g/1 lb	small potatoes	1 lb
225g/½ lb	black pudding, sliced	½ lb
2 tbsp	sunflower oil	2 tbsp
1 small	onion, chopped	1 small
115g/4oz	button mushrooms	2 cups
115g/4oz	cherry tomatoes, halved	2 cups
2 tbsp	chopped fresh parsley	2 tbsp

1. Boil the potatoes until tender. Drain, cool and cut into thick slices.
2. Fry the black pudding in half the oil in a shallow frying pan until just cooked. Remove from the pan.
3. Add the onion and mushrooms to the pan and fry until the onion is translucent. Remove from the pan.
4. Heat the remaining oil in the pan and fry the potatoes over a moderate heat until crisp and golden.
5. Return the black pudding and onion mixture to the pan and add the cherry tomatoes. Stir the mixture for about 2 minutes.
6. Serve on a heated serving dish, sprinkled with the parsley.

BREAKFAST KIDNEYS

Serves 4

Fe	Fol	B$_{12}$
7.8	54	49.5

Metric/Imperial		*American*
4	lambs' kidneys, halved, cored and skinned	4
30g/1oz	butter	2 tbsp
115g/4oz	button mushrooms	2 cups
dash of	Worcestershire sauce	dash of
4 slices	wholemeal bread, toasted	4 slices

1. Cut the kidneys into small chunks.
2. Melt the butter in a shallow non-stick frying pan over a gentle heat. Add the kidneys and fry for 1 minute. Remove the kidneys and set aside.
3. Add the mushrooms to the pan and cook for 5 minutes.
4. Add the Worcestershire sauce, return the kidneys to the pan, and cook for 1 minute.
5. Serve on the freshly prepared wholemeal toast. Grilled tomatoes go very well with this dish.

BRUNCH LOAF

Makes 12 slices

	Fe	Fol	B$_{12}$
	1.6	23	0.35

Metric/Imperial		*American*
55g/2oz	Bran-Buds	1¹/₄ cups
140ml/¹/₄ pint	milk	²/₃ cup
115g/4oz	margarine	¹/₂ cup
115g/4oz	caster sugar	²/₃ cup
2	eggs, lightly beaten	2
85g/3oz	dried apricots, chopped	¹/₂ cup
85g/3oz	dried prunes, stoned and chopped	¹/₂ cup
55g/2oz	hazelnuts, chopped	¹/₂ cup
115g/4oz	self-raising flour	1 cup

1. Pour the cereal into a basin and add the milk. Leave the mixture to stand for 30 minutes.
2. Put the margarine into a large mixing bowl and add the sugar. Using a hand-held electric whisk, cream the mixture until light and fluffy.
3. Gradually beat in the eggs. Stir in the fruit and nuts and the soaked cereal. Gently fold in the flour.
4. Pour the mixture into a non-stick or lightly greased and lined 900g/2 lb loaf tin.
5. Bake in a preheated oven at 180°C/350°F/gas mark 4 for 1–1¹/₄ hours. Leave the loaf to stand for 15 minutes, then turn onto a cooling rack.
6. When cooled, cut slices as required. The loaf will keep for up to 1 week if wrapped in aluminium foil.

Anaemia

EGGY BREAD AND TOMATOES

Fe	Fol	B$_{12}$
3.8	80	1.27

Serves 1

Metric/Imperial		*American*
2	tomatoes, halved	2
1	egg	1
	freshly ground black pepper	
2 slices	wholemeal bread, halved	2 slices
4 tbsp	sunflower oil	4 tbsp

1. Cook the tomato halves under a hot grill or in a microwave oven.
2. Crack the egg into a small basin and season with pepper. Pour the egg mixture onto a plate.
3. Dip the bread in the egg and drain any excess back onto the plate.
4. Heat the oil in a shallow frying pan and fry the eggy bread over a moderate heat for 2 minutes on each side.
5. Serve immediately on a hot plate.

FRUIT AND BRAN BREAKFAST

Fe	Fol	B$_{12}$
7.9	60	0.06

Serves 1

Metric/Imperial		*American*
55g/2oz	dried dates, stoned and chopped	1/3 cup
55g/2oz	dried apricots, chopped	1/3 cup
55g/2oz	dried figs, chopped	1/3 cup
55g/2oz	dried prunes, stoned and chopped	1/3 cup
4 tbsp	freshly squeezed orange juice	4 tbsp
2 tbsp	natural (plain) yogurt	2 tbsp
1 tbsp	coarse bran	1 tbsp

1. Put the dried fruit in a small mixing bowl and pour over the orange juice.
2. Cover and chill for 8 hours or overnight.
3. Pour the soaked fruit and juices into a serving dish. Swirl in the yogurt and sprinkle with the bran.

HERRINGS IN OATS

Serves 4

Fe	Fol	B$_{12}$
1.1	12	3.60

Metric/Imperial		*American*
4 medium	herring fillets	4 medium
1 tbsp	lemon juice	1 tbsp
	freshly ground black pepper	
55g/2oz	oats	1/2 cup
30g/1oz	butter	2 tbsp
2 tbsp	sunflower oil	2 tbsp
4	lemon wedges	4

1. Dip the herring fillets in the lemon juice and sprinkle with pepper.
2. Press the oats onto the fillets.
3. Heat the butter and oil in a shallow frying pan and fry the fish for 5 minutes on each side.
4. Serve with the lemon wedges and crusty wholemeal bread.

KEDGEREE

Serves 4

	Fe	Fol	B$_{12}$
	1.7	21	0.70

Metric/Imperial   *American*

Metric/Imperial		American
225g/8oz	smoked haddock	1/2 lb
170g/6oz	Patna rice	3/4 cup
15g/1/2oz	butter	1 tbsp
2 tsp	curry powder	2 tsp
1 tbsp	chopped fresh parsley	1 tbsp
1	egg, hardboiled and sliced	1

1. Cook the haddock by poaching or in a microwave oven. Drain, remove any skin and bones and flake the flesh.
2. Cook the rice according to the instructions on the packet.
3. Melt the butter in a large pan over a gentle heat. Add the rice, flaked fish, curry powder and parsley. Cover, and shake the mixture in the pan for 1 minute.
4. Serve the kedgeree in a hot serving dish, garnished with the slices of egg.

Note to Cooks

Can be frozen at stage 3.

MUESLI

Serves 1

Fe	Fol	B$_{12}$
4.1	75	0.06

Metric/Imperial		*American*
2 tbsp	oat flakes	2 tbsp
1	eating apple	1
2 tbsp	hazelnuts, chopped	2 tbsp
1 tbsp	chopped dried figs	1 tbsp
1 tbsp	stoned and chopped dried dates	1 tbsp
1 tbsp	freshly squeezed orange juice	1 tbsp
2 tbsp	natural (plain) yogurt	2 tbsp
1 tbsp	wheatgerm	1 tbsp

1. Put the oat flakes in a mixing bowl. Cover with cold water and leave to soak for 8 hours or overnight. Drain thoroughly and tip into a serving dish.
2. Peel and core the apple, then grate the flesh into the mixture.
3. Add the hazelnuts, dried fruit, orange juice and yogurt.
4. Serve sprinkled with the wheatgerm.

SAUSAGE AND BACON PANCAKES

Fe	Fol	B$_{12}$
2.4	31	1.38

Serves 4

Metric/Imperial		*American*
4 rashers	rindless streaky bacon, chopped	4 slices
4 large	pork sausages, sliced	4 large
115g/4oz	brown flour	1 cup
2	eggs	2
140ml/¼ pint	milk	⅔ cup
2 tbsp	sunflower oil	2 tbsp
	freshly ground black pepper	

1. Put the bacon and sausages into a non-stick frying pan and fry for 5 minutes over a gentle heat.
2. Sift the flour into a large mixing bowl and tip in any remaining bran. Make a well in the centre.
3. Drop the eggs into the well and gradually beat into the flour.
4. As the mixture begins to look like a paste, add half the milk. When all the flour has been incorporated add the remaining milk and beat thoroughly.
5. Put the bacon and sausage mixture into the batter and mix well. Heat a film of oil in a shallow non-stick frying pan. Pour in 3 tablespoons of the mixture and cook over a moderate heat for 2 minutes. Turn the

pancakes over and continue cooking for a further 2 minutes. Put the cooked pancakes on a hot plate and keep warm until the batch is ready. Serve hot with a sprinkling of black pepper.

Note to Cooks
Can be frozen.

5

Light Meals and Snacks

AUBERGINE (EGGPLANT) BAKE

Fe	Fol	B$_{12}$
1.0	42	0.17

Serves 4

Metric/Imperial		American
2 medium	aubergines (eggplants)	2 medium
1 tbsp	salt	1 tbsp
1 tbsp	sunflower oil	1 tbsp
1	onion, finely diced	1
4 large	garlic cloves, crushed	4 large
4 rashers	rindless streaky bacon, chopped	4 slices
2 medium	tomatoes, skinned, seeded and chopped	2 medium
115g/4oz	brown rice, cooked	2/3 cup
2 tbsp	chopped fresh chives	2 tbsp
55g/2oz	Cheddar cheese, grated	1/2 cup
	Parmesan cheese, grated	

1. Cut the aubergines (eggplants) in half lengthways. Scoop out the flesh, leaving a 2cm/³⁄₄-inch shell. Sprinkle salt over the flesh and inside the shells. Leave for 30 minutes.

2. Put the flesh in a sieve (strainer) and rinse under cold running water. Also rinse the shells under cold running water.

3. Heat the oil in a shallow non-stick frying pan, add the onion, garlic and bacon and fry over a gentle heat for 5 minutes until the onion has softened.

4. Add the tomatoes and the aubergine (eggplant) flesh and continue cooking for a further 2 minutes. Stir in the rice and chives.

5. Arrange the aubergine (eggplant) shells in an oven-proof dish. Pile the mixture into the shells and sprinkle with the grated cheese.

6. Bake in a preheated oven at 180°C/350°F/gas mark 4 for 20–25 minutes.

7. Serve hot sprinkled with Parmesan cheese.

BEEF AND BEAN BURGERS

Serves 4

	Fe	Fol	B$_{12}$
	5.6	49	2.28

Metric/Imperial		*American*
455g/1 lb	lean minced beef	1 lb
140g/5oz	drained canned red kidney beans, roughly chopped	3/4 cup
1/2	Spanish onion, grated	1/2
2	garlic cloves, crushed	2
dash of	Worcestershire sauce	dash of
dash of	Tabasco	dash of
2 tbsp	chopped fresh parsley	2 tbsp
4	wholemeal buns	4
2 tbsp	sunflower oil	2 tbsp
4 leaves	Cos lettuce, shredded	4 leaves
2 medium	tomatoes, sliced	2 medium

1. Put the minced beef into a large mixing bowl.
2. Add the kidney beans, onion, garlic, Worcestershire sauce, Tabasco and parsley. Stir the mixture well.
3. Work the mixture together into a sausage shape, then form into 4 large rounds about 2.5cm/1 inch thick.
4. Heat the oil in a shallow non-stick frying pan and cook the burgers for 6 minutes on each side over a moderate heat.
5. Serve in the buns with the lettuce and tomatoes.

PASTA CARBONARA

Serves 1

Fe	Fol	B$_{12}$
2.9	50	1.60

Metric/Imperial		*American*
4 rashers	streaky bacon, rindless	4 slices
55g/2oz	pasta shapes	1 cup
1	egg	1
30g/1oz	Cheddar cheese, grated	1/4 cup
1 tbsp	chopped fresh parsley	1 tbsp
	freshly ground black pepper	

1. Warm a serving bowl.
2. Cut the bacon into 1cm/1/2 inch pieces. Fry in a non-stick shallow frying pan over a gentle heat until golden brown.
3. Cook the pasta following the instructions on the packet. Drain thoroughly.
4. Meanwhile, beat the egg in the warm serving bowl and stir in the cheese, parsley and pepper.
5. Tip the hot pasta into the egg mixture and toss until the pasta is thoroughly coated with the egg mixture.
6. Pour the hot cooked bacon and any fat from the pan over the pasta. Toss once more and eat immediately.

CORNED BEEF HASH

Serves 4

Fe	Fol	B$_{12}$
3.9	45	2.28

Metric/Imperial		*American*
4 medium	potatoes	4 medium
1 tbsp	sunflower oil	1 tbsp
2 medium	onions, finely sliced	2 medium
455g/1 lb	corned beef, diced	1 lb
1/2 tsp	dried mixed herbs	1/2 tsp

1. Cook the potatoes in their skins until tender. Drain, remove the skins and roughly chop the flesh.
2. Heat the oil in a shallow non-stick frying pan. Add the onions and cook over a gentle heat for 5 minutes.
3. Add the potato and continue cooking for a further 10 minutes.
4. Stir in the corned beef and herbs and cook for 5 more minutes.
5. Serve the hash piled up on a hot serving dish, accompanied by a tomato-flavoured dish such as baked beans in tomato sauce, grilled tomatoes or a chunky tomato sauce.

JACKET POTATOES WITH FILLINGS

Fe	Fol	B₁₂

Fe	Fol	B_{12}
0.4	24	0

Serves 1

Metric/Imperial		*American*
1 medium	potato	1 medium

Fillings

Fe	Fol	B_{12}
0.5	18	0.61

| 55g/2oz | Cheddar cheese, grated | ½ cup |
| 2 tsp | French mustard | 2 tsp |

Fe	Fol	B_{12}
0.9	11	0.17

55g/2oz	cooked chicken, diced	⅓ cup
1 tbsp	mayonnaise	1 tbsp
1 tbsp	sultanas	1 tbsp

Fe	Fol	B_{12}
1.5	13	0.55

| 55g/2oz | cooked pork sausage, sliced | ⅓ cup |
| 2 tbsp | baked beans in tomato sauce | 2 tbsp |

Fe	Fol	B$_{12}$
1.0	1	2.81

55g/2oz	canned tuna fish, drained and flaked	1/3 cup
1 tbsp	mayonnaise	1 tbsp

1. Pierce the potato in several places with the point of a sharp knife.
2. Bake for about 1 hour in a preheated oven at 200°C/400°F/gas mark 6. Alternatively cook in a microwave oven following the manufacturer's instructions.
3. Cut the potato in half lengthways and scoop out the flesh, taking care to leave the skin intact.
4. Mash the flesh in a basin and mix with the selected filling.
5. Pile the mixture into the potato shells and put into an ovenproof dish. Continue cooking for 10 minutes in a conventional oven or the equivalent time in a microwave.

MUSHROOM AND
LIVER PÂTÉ OMELETTE

Fe	Fol	B$_{12}$
5.8	163	4.95

Not suitable for pregnant women

Serves 1

Metric/Imperial		American
1 tsp	sunflower oil	1 tsp
225g/8oz	button mushrooms	½ lb
30g/1oz	coarse liver pâté	2 tbsp
1	spring onion, cut into strips	1
2	eggs	2
2 tsp	water	2 tsp
7g/¼oz	butter	½ tbsp

1. Heat the oil in a shallow non-stick frying pan, add the mushrooms and cook for 5 minutes over a moderate heat.
2. Add the pâté and the spring onion and continue cooking for a further 2 minutes. Cover and set aside.
3. Melt the butter in a shallow non-stick frying pan. Beat the eggs and water together and pour into the pan.
4. Before the mixture sets, using a spatula, pull the edges towards the centre to let the uncooked liquid run underneath the omelette. Tilt the pan over the heat until the mixture is just set.
5. Fold the omelette in half, slide onto a hot serving dish and top with the mushroom mixture. Serve at once.

QUICK PIZZA

Serves 4

	Fe	Fol	B$_{12}$
	2.3	65	0.65

Metric/Imperial   *American*

Scone base

115g/4oz	wholemeal self-raising flour	1 cup
1/2 tsp	baking powder	1/2 tsp
30g/1oz	polyunsaturated margarine	2 tbsp
1/2 tsp	dried mixed herbs	1/2 tsp
1	egg, beaten	1
1 tbsp	milk	1 tbsp

Topping

1 tbsp	sunflower oil	1 tbsp
1 small	onion, finely chopped	1 small
115g/4oz	mushrooms, sliced	2 cups
4 medium	tomatoes, skinned, seeded and chopped	4 medium
1 tbsp	tomato purée	1 tbsp
1 tsp	dried oregano	1 tsp
115g/4oz	Cheddar cheese, grated	1 cup
30g/1oz	black olives, stoned, pitted and halved	1/4 cup

1. To make the scone base, sift together the flour and baking powder into a large mixing bowl. Add the remaining scone base ingredients. Mix well together using a wooden spoon until a soft dough has formed.
2. Turn the dough onto a lightly floured work surface and knead gently.

3. Shape into a round about 25cm/10 inches in diameter and flatten using a rolling pin.
4. Place the scone base on a non-stick or lightly greased baking sheet.
5. To make the topping, heat the oil in a shallow frying pan and fry the onion over a gentle heat until softened.
6. Add the mushrooms and continue cooking for 2 more minutes. Stir in the tomatoes, tomato purée and oregano.
7. Spread the mixture evenly over the scone base. Sprinkle with the grated cheese and decorate with the olives.
8. Bake in a preheated oven at 200°C/400°F/gas mark 6 for 25–30 minutes.
9. Serve hot or cold with a green salad.

SALOUSA

Serves 4

	Fe	Fol	B₁₂

Fe	Fol	B_{12}
1.7	14	0

Metric/Imperial		*American*
225g/½ lb	drained canned chickpeas	1 cup
1 tbsp	tahini paste	1 tbsp
2	garlic cloves, crushed	2
2 tbsp	chopped fresh coriander	2 tbsp
3 tbsp	olive oil	3 tbsp
1 tbsp	lemon juice	1 tbsp
	freshly ground black pepper	

1. Put the chickpeas, tahini paste and garlic into a liquidizer or food processor and process for 30 seconds until roughly blended.
2. Pour the mixture into a mixing bowl, add the coriander and oil and mix well. Stir in the lemon juice and pepper.
3. Spoon the mixture into a serving bowl. Chill for 1 hour.
4. Serve with warm pitta bread.

SCRAMBLES ON TOAST

Serves 1

Fe	Fol	B$_{12}$
3.2	70	2.61

Metric/Imperial		*American*
2	eggs	2
1 tbsp	milk	1 tbsp
	freshly ground black pepper	
15g/½oz	butter	1 tbsp
1 slice	wholemeal bread, toasted	1 slice

Additions

Fe	Fol	B$_{12}$
6.6	43	43.45

55g/2oz	kidneys, sautéed	¼ cup

Fe	Fol	B$_{12}$
0.8	1	0

55g/2oz	streaky bacon, grilled and diced	¼ cup

Fe	Fol	B$_{12}$
0.2	18	0.61

55g/2oz	Cheddar cheese, grated	¼ cup

1. Crack the eggs into a small basin. Add the milk and pepper and beat well.
2. Heat the butter in a non-stick saucepan over a gentle heat, pour in the egg mixture and stir continuously until set.
3. Stir in the chosen addition and pile the scramble onto the freshly cooked wholemeal toast.
4. Serve at once.

Light Meals and Snacks

SPINACH AND CHEESE FILO

Serves 4

Fe	Fol	B₁₂
2.5	178	0.13

Metric/Imperial		*American*
455g/1 lb	spinach, trimmed	1 lb
1 tbsp	sunflower oil	1 tbsp
1 small	onion, finely chopped	1 small
2	garlic cloves, crushed	2
170g/6oz	curd cheese	3/4 cup
	freshly ground black pepper	
pinch	nutmeg, grated	pinch
2	sheets filo pastry	2
1 tbsp	butter, melted	1 tbsp

1. Blanch the spinach in boiling water, drain well and chop. Squeeze out any excess moisture.
2. Heat the oil in a pan, add the onion and garlic and fry over a gentle heat until softened.
3. Put the spinach, onion mixture and curd cheese into a mixing bowl. Add the pepper and nutmeg and mix thoroughly.
4. Cut each sheet of pastry into 4 squares and brush with some of the melted butter.
5. Spoon the spinach mixture onto the pastry. Roll the pastry up into cylinder shapes.
6. Brush with the remaining melted butter and bake in a preheated oven at 200°C/400°F/gas mark 6 for about 15 minutes.
7. Serve hot with a mixed salad.

TUNA AND LENTIL SALAD

Fe	Fol	B$_{12}$
7.0	65	2.70

Serves 4

Metric/Imperial		*American*
225g/8oz	canned tuna fish, drained	1/2 lb
1 small	onion, chopped	1 small
3 tbsp	French dressing	3 tbsp
225g/8oz	brown lentils	1/2 lb

1. Flake the tuna fish in a mixing bowl and add the onion and French dressing. Cover and keep chilled.
2. Put the lentils in a large saucepan and cover with cold water. Bring to boiling point, cover and simmer for 30 minutes or until the lentils are tender. Drain thoroughly.
3. Mix the hot lentils with the tuna fish mixture and serve warm, with chunks of crusty bread.

6

Starters

ANCHOVY TOAST

Serves 4

	Fe	Fol	B$_{12}$
	2.0	27	1.65

Metric/Imperial		*American*
20	canned anchovy fillets	20
2	garlic cloves, crushed	2
1 tbsp	lemon juice	1 tbsp
	freshly ground black pepper	
2 tbsp	olive oil	2 tbsp
8 x 5cm/ 2-inch slices	French bread, toasted	8 x 5cm/ 2-in slices
2 tbsp	black olives, stoned, pitted and chopped	2 tbsp

1. Rinse the anchovies under running water and drain thoroughly.
2. Put the anchovies in a liquidizer or food processor and process until smooth. Spoon the paste into a mixing bowl.
3. Add the garlic, lemon juice and pepper and stir well.

4. Dribble the olive oil into the mixture and continue stirring.
5. Spread the anchovy paste on the toasted French bread and serve garnished with the black olives.

AUBERGINE (EGGPLANT) DIP

Fe	Fol	B_{12}
0.7	32	0.17

Serves 4

Metric/Imperial		American
2 medium	aubergines (eggplants), sliced	2 medium
2 tbsp	salt	2 tbsp
2 tbsp	olive oil	2 tbsp
2 medium	onions, grated	2 medium
3	garlic cloves, crushed	3
2	canned anchovy fillets, chopped	2
	freshly ground black pepper	
2 tbsp	chopped fresh basil	2 tbsp
1 tbsp	lemon juice	1 tbsp

1. Sprinkle the aubergine (eggplant) slices with the salt. Leave to stand for 1 hour. Rinse under cold running water, drain and pat dry with kitchen paper.
2. Arrange the aubergines (eggplants) on an oiled baking dish and sprinkle with the olive oil. Bake in a preheated oven at 190°C/375°F/gas mark 5 for about 1 hour or until soft.
3. Place the cooked aubergines (eggplants) in a liquidizer or food processor and process. Tip the aubergine (eggplant) paste into a mixing bowl.
4. Add the onions, garlic, anchovies and pepper to the bowl, stir well and chill for 1 hour.
5. Serve sprinkled with the basil and lemon juice, accompanied by sticks of carrot, cucumber and fennel.

BROCCOLI SOUP

Serves 4

Fe	Fol	B$_{12}$
2.3	111	0.03

Metric/Imperial		*American*
455g/1 lb	broccoli	1 lb
1 tbsp	sunflower oil	1 tbsp
1	onion, chopped	1
1.1 litres/ 2 pints	vegetable stock	5 cups
2tbsp	ground almonds	2 tbsp
4 tbsp	double cream	4 tbsp
	freshly grated nutmeg

1. Separate the broccoli florets and stalks and wash in a colander under running water. Drain well.
2. Heat the oil in a pan and fry the onion over a gentle heat until softened.
3. Add the vegetable stock and bring to boiling point.
4. Add the broccoli, cover and simmer for 12 minutes until the broccoli has softened.
5. Pour the mixture into a liquidizer or food processor and process until smooth.
6. Return the mixture to the pan and stir in the ground almonds.
7. Bring the soup to boiling point, stir in the cream and nutmeg and serve immediately.

CHICKEN LIVER PÂTÉ

Not suitable for pregnant women.

Fe	Fol	B$_{12}$
11.0	674	63.70

Serves 4

Metric/Imperial		*American*
455g/1 lb	chicken livers	1 lb
225g/8oz	unsalted butter	½ lb
1 small	onion, grated	1 small
2 large	garlic cloves, crushed	2 large
2 tbsp	brandy	2 tbsp
4	bay leaves	4

1. Pick the chicken livers over; wash and pat dry with kitchen paper.
2. Melt 30g (1oz) of the butter in a frying pan. Add the onion and garlic and fry over a gentle heat until softened.
3. Transfer the onion mixture to a liquidizer or food processor.
4. Turn the heat up under the frying pan and fry the chicken livers quickly to brown them. After 3 minutes pour in the brandy.
5. Add the cooked chicken livers to the mixture in the liquidizer. Blend until smooth.
6. Pour the mixture into a pâté dish and smooth the surface using a palette knife. Leave to cool.
7. Melt the remaining butter in a clean pan and pour this over the surface of the pâté.
8. Garnish with the bay leaves and serve with slices of wholewheat toast or crusty bread.

Anaemia

CRUNCHY PARSNIP STICKS

Serves 4

Fe	Fol	B$_{12}$
2.0	79	0.71

Metric/Imperial   *American*

3 medium	parsnips	3 medium
2	eggs	2
2 tbsp	wholemeal flour	2 tbsp
115g/4oz	stale wholemeal breadcrumbs	1 cup

Dip

1 tbsp	horseradish sauce	1 tbsp
140 ml/¼ pint	natural (plain) yogurt	⅔ cup
	sunflower oil, for deep frying	

1. Peel and trim the parsnips and cut into thin sticks.
2. Beat the eggs in a small basin. Dip the parsnip sticks in the egg, drain off any excess then toss in the flour.
3. Dip the floured parsnip sticks into the egg once more, drain off any excess and toss in the breadcrumbs.
4. Make the dip by combining the horseradish sauce and yogurt in a bowl. Set aside.
5. Heat the oil in a deep frying pan. Deep-fry the parsnip sticks until golden brown, then drain and tip onto kitchen paper.
6. Place on a heated serving dish and serve immediately, accompanied by the horseradish and yogurt dip.

CURRIED LENTIL SOUP

Serves 4

Fe	Fol	B$_{12}$
4.5	22	0

Metric/Imperial		*American*
1 tbsp	sunflower oil	1 tbsp
1 medium	onion, finely chopped	1 medium
1 tbsp	curry paste	1 tbsp
2 medium	carrots, finely chopped	2 medium
170g/6oz	split red lentils	1 cup
850ml/1½ pints	vegetable stock	3¾ cups
30g/1oz	creamed coconut	2 tbsp
4	lemon slices	4

1. Put the oil into a large heavy-based saucepan and warm over a gentle heat. Add the onion and fry until beginning to brown.
2. Stir in the curry paste and continue cooking for 1 minute.
3. Add the carrots, lentils and stock. Bring to the boil, cover and simmer for 40 minutes.
4. Stir in the creamed coconut and continue cooking for 3 minutes.
5. Pour into individual hot soup bowls, garnish with the lemon slices and serve with naan bread.

GUACAMOLE-STYLE DIP

Fe	Fol	B₁₂
0.7	20	0

Serves 4

Metric/Imperial   *American*

2 medium	avocado pears	2 medium
1 large	garlic clove, crushed	1 large
1 small	onion, finely chopped	1 small
225g/8oz	tomatoes, skinned, seeded and chopped	1/2 lb
2 tsp	lemon juice	2 tsp
2 tsp	olive oil	2 tsp
1/2 tsp	chilli powder	1/2 tsp

1. Cut the avocado pears in half lengthways, remove the stone and skin, and roughly chop the flesh.
2. Put the garlic, onion, tomatoes, avocado flesh, lemon juice, oil and chilli powder into a mixing bowl, and blend with a fork.
3. Pour into individual serving dishes. Chill for 30 minutes.
4. Serve with sticks of freshly prepared vegetables such as carrot, celery, green pepper.

LEEK AND TATTIE SOUP

Serves 4

Fe	Fol	B$_{12}$
1.1	73	0.34

Metric/Imperial		*American*
15g/^{1}/$_{2}$oz	butter	1 tbsp
455g/1 lb	leeks, sliced	1 lb
455g/1 lb	potatoes, roughly chopped	1 lb
570ml/1 pint	vegetable stock	2^{1}/$_{2}$ cups
340ml/^{2}/$_{3}$ pint	milk	1^{1}/$_{2}$ cups
	white pepper	
1 tbsp	chopped fresh chives	1 tbsp

1. Melt the butter in a heavy saucepan, add the leeks and potatoes and cook over a gentle heat for about 5 minutes.
2. Add the stock, bring to the boil, then cover and simmer for about 30 minutes. Pour into a liquidizer or food processor and process until smooth.
3. Pour the mixture into a clean pan, add the milk and pepper, and cook over a gentle heat for 5 minutes.
4. Serve hot sprinkled with the chopped chives.

SMOKED MACKEREL PÂTÉ

Fe	Fol	B12
1.6	15	15.33

Serves 4

Metric/Imperial		*American*
4 medium	smoked mackerel fillets	4 medium
1 tbsp	lemon juice	1 tbsp
170g/6oz	cottage cheese	3/4 cup
60ml/2fl oz	natural (plain) yogurt	1/4 cup
1 tbsp	chopped fresh dill	1 tbsp
4	lemon wedges	4

1. Skin and bone the mackerel fillets, then flake the flesh.
2. Put the flesh in a liquidizer or food processor with the lemon juice, cottage cheese, yogurt and dill. Process until smooth.
3. Spoon the mixture into a pâté dish and smooth the surface with a knife. Garnish with the lemon wedges, and chill for 1 hour before serving with crusty wholemeal bread.

SPICY PARSNIP SOUP

Serves 4

Fe	Fol	B$_{12}$
1.5	82	0.34

Metric/Imperial		*American*
1 tbsp	sunflower oil	1 tbsp
455g/1 lb	parsnips, coarsely chopped	1 lb
1 large	onion, sliced	1 large
1 heaped tsp	curry powder	1 heaped tsp
570ml/1 pint	vegetable stock	2$\frac{1}{2}$ cups
340ml/$\frac{2}{3}$ pint	milk	1$\frac{1}{2}$ cups
2 heaped tbsp	chopped fresh coriander	2 heaped tbsp

1. Heat the oil in a heavy saucepan. Add the parsnip and onion and fry over a gentle heat for about 5 minutes.
2. Sprinkle on the curry powder and continue cooking for a further 5 minutes.
3. Add the vegetable stock, bring to the boil, cover and simmer for 1 hour.
4. Pour into a liquidizer or food processor and process until smooth.
5. Pour the mixture into a clean pan, add the milk and cook over a gentle heat for 5 minutes.
6. Serve hot, sprinkled with the chopped coriander.

STEAK AND KIDNEY SOUP

Serves 4

Fe	Fol	B₁₂
4.7	57	17.00

Metric/Imperial		*American*
45g/1½oz	margarine	3 tbsp
225g/½ lb	lean stewing steak, cubed	½ lb
225g/½ lb	ox kidney, trimmed	½ lb
2 medium	onions, roughly chopped	2 medium
1.1 litres/ 2 pints	beef stock	5 cups
1	bouquet garni	1
1 tbsp	flour	1 tbsp
1 tbsp	tomato purée	1 tbsp

1. Heat one-third of the margarine in a flameproof casserole, and fry the steak and kidney over a moderate heat until browned. Remove from the casserole and set aside.
2. Add the onions to the casserole and cook for about 5 minutes until beginning to turn golden brown.
3. Return the steak and kidney to the casserole and add the stock and bouquet garni. Bring to the boil, cover and simmer for 2–2½ hours. Skim periodically.
4. Remove the bouquet garni, and purée the soup, in batches, in a liquidizer or food processor until smooth.
5. Wipe the casserole out with kitchen paper. Melt the remaining margarine in the casserole over a moderate heat, stir in the flour, and cook until brown, stirring continuously. Gradually blend in the processed mixture and the tomato purée.

Starters

6. Serve in a hot soup tureen, accompanied by crusty granary bread.

7

Main Protein Dishes

BEEF AND MUSHROOM CASEROLE WITH STOUT

Fe	Fol	B$_{12}$
3.1	51	2.35

Serves 4

Metric/Imperial		*American*
455g/1 lb	lean stewing steak, cubed	1 lb
2 large	onions, sliced	2 large
225g/8oz	button mushrooms	1/2 lb
1 tbsp	sunflower oil	1 tbsp
2 tbsp	flour	2 tbsp
285ml/1/2 pint	stout	1 1/3 cups
2	bay leaves	2

1. Heat the oil in a heavy-based flameproof casserole and add the meat. Fry over a moderate heat for 5 minutes, turning the pieces to ensure even cooking. Remove the meat from the casserole and set aside.
2. Add the onions and mushrooms to the casserole and fry over a moderate heat for about 5 minutes.

3. Stir in the flour, then add the meat, stout and bay leaves. Mix thoroughly.
4. Cover and cook in a preheated oven at 180°C/350°F/gas mark 4 for 2½ hours.
5. Serve piping hot with a selection of vegetables.

MINTY LAMB BURGERS

Serves 4

	Fe	Fol	B$_{12}$
	2.9	26	2.59

Metric/Imperial		*American*
455g/1 lb	lean lamb, minced	1 lb
1 small	onion, finely chopped	1 small
4 tbsp	chopped fresh mint	4 tbsp
55g/2oz	fresh brown breadcrumbs	1 cup
½	lemon, grated zest of	½
1	egg, beaten	1
2 tbsp	brown flour	2 tbsp
1 tbsp	sunflower oil	1 tbsp

1. In a large mixing bowl, combine the lamb, onion, mint, breadcrumbs, lemon zest and egg.
2. Mix thoroughly then shape into 8 burgers and coat with the flour.
3. Heat the oil in a non-stick shallow frying pan. Fry the burgers over a moderate heat for 5 minutes on each side.
4. Serve immediately with a mixed salad and new potatoes with a yogurt dressing.

SAUSAGE AND BEAN CASSEROLE

Fe	Fol	B$_{12}$
4.8	25	1.14

Serves 4

Metric/Imperial		*American*
455g/1 lb	pork sausages	1 lb
1 medium	onion, finely sliced	1 medium
565g/1¼ lb	drained, canned red kidney beans	3 cups
225g/8oz	canned chopped tomatoes	1¹/₃ cups
1 tbsp	tomato purée	1 tbsp
285ml/¹/₂ pint	dry cider	1¹/₃ cups
1	bouquet garni	1

1. Fry the sausages in a shallow non-stick frying pan for 6 minutes until browned. Remove from the pan and cut into chunks.
2. Fry the onion in the sausage fat until just golden brown. Using kitchen paper take off any surplus fat from the onions.
3. Put the sausages, onion, kidney beans, tomatoes, tomato purée, cider and bouquet garni into a large flameproof casserole.
4. Bring to the boil, then cover and simmer for 20 minutes. Remove the bouquet garni.
5. Serve hot with jacket potatoes and a green salad.

Note to Cooks

Can be frozen.

SWEET AND SOUR PORK

Serves 4

Fe	Fol	B$_{12}$
2.1	28	3.41

Metric/Imperial		*American*
2 tbsp	cornflour	2 tbsp
2 tbsp	caster sugar	2 tbsp
2 tbsp	white wine vinegar	2 tbsp
2 tbsp	fresh orange juice	2 tbsp
3 tbsp	soya sauce	3 tbsp
2 tbsp	tomato purée	2 tbsp
2 tbsp	medium sherry	2 tbsp
6 tbsp	water	6 tbsp
455g/1 lb	lean pork, cubed	1 lb
1 tbsp	sunflower oil	1 tbsp
1 medium	green pepper, seeded and sliced	1 medium

1. Put the cornflour, sugar, vinegar, orange juice, soya sauce, tomato purée, sherry and water into a large mixing bowl. Blend until smooth.
2. Heat the oil in a shallow frying pan. Add the pork and cook over a moderate heat for 6 minutes, turning frequently.
3. Add the pepper and continue cooking for 2 minutes.
4. Reduce the heat, add the cornflour mixture and stir continuously for about 5 minutes until the sauce becomes thickened and translucent. Cover and simmer for 10 minutes.
5. Serve with plain boiled rice.

Main Protein Dishes

CHICKEN PILAFF

	Fe	Fol	B$_{12}$
	3.3	44	0

Serves 4

Metric/Imperial		*American*
1 tbsp	sunflower oil	1 tbsp
1 medium	onion, chopped	1 medium
2 large	garlic cloves, crushed	2 large
1/4 tsp	ground allspice	1/4 tsp
1/4 tsp	ground cinnamon	1/4 tsp
55g/2oz	pine nuts	3 1/2 tbsp
225g/8oz	brown easy-cook rice	1/2 lb
570ml/1 pint	chicken stock	2 1/2 cups
455g/1 lb	cooked chicken, diced	1 lb
55g/2oz	seedless raisins	1/3 cup
55g/2oz	dried apricots, chopped	1/3 cup
2 tbsp	chopped fresh parsley	2 tbsp

1. Heat the oil in a large flameproof casserole, add the onion and fry until lightly browned.
2. Add the garlic, allspice, cinnamon and pine nuts and cook for 1 minute.
3. Stir in the rice and stock and bring to boiling point. Reduce the heat, cover and simmer for 30 minutes or until the liquid has been absorbed.
4. Add the chicken, raisins and apricots and stir into the rice mixture. Leave over the heat for a further 2 minutes.
5. Serve sprinkled with the chopped fresh parsley.

CHICKEN SATÉ

Serves 4

	Fe	Fol	B$_{12}$
	2.3	52	0

Metric/Imperial		*American*
4	chicken breasts	4
1 tsp	ground turmeric	1 tsp
2 tbsp	lemon juice	2 tbsp
55g/2oz	desiccated coconut	2/3 cup
285ml/1/2 pint	boiling water	11/3 cups
1 tbsp	groundnut oil	1 tbsp
1 small	onion, finely chopped	1 small
1 tsp	chilli powder	1 tsp
1 tsp	soft brown sugar	1 tsp
115g/4oz	peanuts, finely chopped	1 cup

1. Remove the skin and bone from the chicken breasts and cut the flesh into thin strips.
2. Place the strips in a bowl with the turmeric and half the lemon juice and mix well.
3. Put the coconut in a bowl and pour on the boiling water. Leave to stand for 20 minutes, then strain and reserve the liquid.
4. Heat the oil in a shallow frying pan and fry the onion over a gentle heat for 5 minutes.
5. Add the chilli powder, sugar and peanuts. Mix well and fry for a further 5 minutes.
6. Add the coconut milk and bring the mixture to boiling point. Simmer for 10 minutes or until thickened. Remove from the heat and add the remaining lemon juice.

Main Protein Dishes

7. Thread the strips of chicken onto skewers. Place under a preheated moderate grill and cook for 3 minutes. Turn and cook for a further 3 minutes.
8. Serve hot or cold with the sauce.

FRUITY CHICKEN

Serves 4

Fe	Fol	B$_{12}$
1.5	49	0.14

Metric/Imperial		*American*
4 medium	chicken breasts	4 medium
2 large	oranges	2 large
85g/3oz	dried apricots, chopped	½ cup
285ml/½ pint	natural (plain) low-fat yogurt	1⅓ cups
1 heaped tbsp	chopped fresh parsley	1 heaped tbsp

1. Roast the chicken breasts. Allow to cool, then remove the skin and bones. Cut the flesh into cubes.
2. Grate the orange zest into a large mixing bowl. Peel and segment the oranges and add to the zest.
3. Add the dried apricots, stir in the yogurt, and gently fold in the cubes of chicken.
4. Chill for 30 minutes, then serve on a platter, sprinkled with the parsley and accompanied by jacket potatoes and a mixed salad.

RABBIT WITH PRUNES

Fe	Fol	B$_{12}$
5.6	11	12.75

serves 4

Metric/Imperial		*American*
Marinade		
570ml/1 pint	red wine	2¹/₂ cups
2	bay leaves	2
1	garlic clove, crushed	1
1 tbsp	sunflower oil	1 tbsp
1	rabbit, jointed and skinned	1
30g/1oz	butter	2 tbsp
1 tbsp	plain flour	1 tbsp
455g/1 lb	dried prunes, stoned	1 lb
2 tbsp	redcurrant jelly	2 tbsp

1. Make the marinade by combining all the ingredients in a large bowl.
2. Put the rabbit joints in the marinade, cover and refrigerate for 24 hours.
3. Remove the rabbit joints and pat dry with kitchen paper. Strain the marinade and set aside.
4. Melt the butter in a flameproof casserole over a gentle heat. Fry the rabbit joints for about 10 minutes, turning occasionally to ensure even browning. Remove and set aside.
5. Add the flour to the pan and stir with the butter and juices until lightly browned.
6. Add the marinade and continue stirring until the sauce has thickened. Return the joints to the casserole.

Anaemia

7. Add the prunes, cover and simmer for 1 hour.
8. Arrange the joints on a hot serving dish and keep warm. Add the redcurrant jelly to the sauce and stir well.
9. Pour the sauce over the rabbit and serve immediately.

KIDNEY KEBABS

Serves 4

Fe	Fol	B$_{12}$
7.1	51	49.50

Metric/Imperial		*American*
4	lamb's kidneys	4
2 tbsp	sunflower oil	2 tbsp
1 tsp	dried rosemary	1 tsp
1 tsp	dried thyme	1 tsp
12	mushroom caps	12
12	cherry tomatoes	12
6	shallots, halved	6

1. Prepare the kidneys by cutting them in half and removing the central core and skin. Cut into quarters.
2. Blend the oil and herbs together. Thread the kidneys and vegetables onto skewers and brush with the oil mixture.
3. Cook under a preheated hot grill for 6 minutes, turning the skewers to ensure even cooking.
4. Serve on a bed of rice with green salad.

LIVER AND BACON KEBABS

Not suitable for pregnant women.

Fe	Fol	B$_{12}$
11.2	252	95.55

Serves 4

Metric/Imperial		*American*
455g/1 lb	lambs' liver, thickly sliced	1 lb
12 rashers	streaky bacon, rindless	12 slices
12	shallots	12
1 tbsp	sunflower oil	1 tbsp

1. Trim the liver removing any visible membranes or ducts and cut into 24 pieces.
2. Cut each bacon rasher (slice) in half lengthways and wrap around the liver pieces.
3. Thread the liver and bacon and the shallots onto 4 large skewers (6 liver and bacon rolls and 3 shallots per skewer).
4. Lightly brush with the oil and cook under a preheated hot grill for 5 minutes on each side.
5. Serve hot on a bed of rice with a selection of salads.

LIVER SCHNITZEL

Fe	Fol	B$_{12}$
11.3	262	95.87

Not suitable for pregnant women.

Serves 4

Metric/Imperial		*American*
455g/1 lb	lambs' liver, sliced	1 lb
30g/1oz	flour	¼ cup
1	egg, beaten	1
55g/2oz	fresh white breadcrumbs	1 cup
1	lemon, zest of	1
2 tbsp	sunflower oil	2 tbsp
2 tbsp	chopped fresh parsley	2 tbsp
4	lemon wedges	4

1. Trim the liver of any ducts and connective tissue.
2. Coat the liver in the flour, then dip in the egg and drain well.
3. Mix the breadcrumbs with the lemon zest and coat the slices of liver with the mixture.
4. Heat the oil in a shallow frying pan and fry the liver for 3 minutes on each side over a moderate heat.
5. Serve garnished with the parsley and lemon wedges, and accompanied by new potatoes and a mixed salad.

LIVER WITH ORANGE

Not suitable for pregnant women.

Fe	Fol	B$_{12}$
10.9	279	95.55

Serves 4

Metric/Imperial		*American*
455g/1 lb	lambs' liver, sliced	1 lb
1 tbsp	flour	1 tbsp
2 medium	oranges	2 medium
1 tbsp	sunflower oil	1 tbsp
2 tbsp	chopped fresh parsley	2 tbsp

1. Trim the liver of any visible membranes or ducts and coat in the flour.
2. Remove the zest from the oranges and put into a mixing bowl. Discard the pith and any seeds, and cut the oranges into segments.
3. Heat the oil in a shallow non-stick frying pan and brown the pieces of liver on both sides, allowing 3 minutes per side.
4. Add the orange zest, segments and parsley to the pan, cover and cook for 1 minute. Serve at once on a bed of Veggie Rice (page 133).

FISH PROVENÇALE

Serves 4

	Fe	Fol	B$_{12}$
	1.1	15	7.0

Metric/Imperial		*American*
4	mackerel fillets	4
225g/8oz	tomatoes, skinned, seeded and roughly chopped	½ lb
1 medium	onion, finely chopped	1 medium
1 large	garlic clove, crushed	1 large
1 tbsp	tomato purée	1 tbsp
1 tsp	wine vinegar	1 tsp
3	bay leaves	3
1	bouquet garni	1
	freshly ground black pepper	

1. Arrange the mackerel fillets skin-side down in a shallow ovenproof dish.
2. Spread the tomatoes and onion over the top of the fish.
3. Put the garlic, tomato purée, vinegar and pepper into a bowl and blend with a fork. Pour the mixture over the fish.
4. Add the bay leaves and bouquet garni, cover and cook in a preheated oven at 220°C/425°F/gas mark 7 for 40 minutes.
5. Serve hot with jacket potatoes and a green salad.

Anaemia

PRAWN AND MUSHROOM COURGETTES (SHRIMP AND MUSHROOM ZUCCHINI)

Fe	Fol	B$_{12}$
1.8	67	0.17

Serves 4

Metric/Imperial		*American*
4	courgettes (zucchini)	4
225g/8oz	shelled cooked prawns	1/2 lb
55g/2oz	Cheddar cheese, grated	1/2 cup
55g/2oz	mushrooms, finely chopped	3/4 cup
30g/1oz	fresh wholemeal breadcrumbs	1/2 cup
30g/1oz	butter	2 tbsp
2 large	garlic cloves, crushed	2 large
1 tbsp	chopped fresh parsley	1 tbsp

1. Cook the courgettes (zucchini) whole until tender by boiling, steaming or in a microwave oven. Drain well.
2. Cut the courgettes (zucchini) in half lengthways and scoop out the flesh.
3. Mix the flesh with the prawns (shrimp), cheese, mushrooms and breadcrumbs, then pack the mixture into the courgette (zucchini) shells.
4. Melt the butter in a shallow frying pan and fry the garlic over a gentle heat for 1 minute.
5. Pour the garlic butter over the filled courgettes (zucchini) and place under a preheated moderate grill for about 5 minutes until the filling is lightly browned.
6. Serve sprinkled with the chopped fresh parsley.

SEAFOOD PIE

Fe	Fol	B₁₂
2.1	63	2.64

Serves 4

Metric/Imperial		American
225g/8oz	cod	1/2 lb
455g/1 lb	smoked haddock	1 lb
30g/1oz	polyunsaturated margarine	2 tbsp
30g/1oz	flour	1/4 cup
285ml/1/2 pint	milk	2/3 cup
115g/4oz	cooked shelled prawns (shrimp)	1 cup
1	egg, hardboiled and chopped	1
2 tbsp	chopped fresh parsley	2 tbsp
455g/1 lb	potatoes, cooked and mashed	2 cups
55g/2oz	Cheddar cheese, grated	1/2 cup

1. Cook the cod and haddock by poaching or in a microwave oven. Strain well.

2. Remove any skin and bones from the fish, and flake the flesh with a fork.

3. Heat the margarine in a non-stick saucepan and stir in the flour.

4. Remove the pan from the heat and gradually stir in the milk, beating until the mixture is smooth.

5. Return the pan to the heat. Bring the sauce to boiling point, stirring constantly to prevent any lumps from forming. Cook for 3 minutes until the sauce is smooth and thickened.

Anaemia

6. Add the prawns (shrimp), flaked fish, egg and parsley and fold the mixture together.
7. Pour the mixture into a shallow ovenproof dish and top with the mashed potato. Smooth the surface then make a pattern, using a fork.
8. Bake in a preheated oven at 220°C/425°F/gas mark 7 for 30 minutes.
9. Sprinkle the cheese on the surface and flash under a preheated hot grill.
10. Serve piping hot with a selection of freshly cooked vegetables.

TUNA FISHCAKES

Fe	Fol	B$_{12}$
2.5	41	3.34

Serves 4

Metric/Imperial		*American*
225g/8oz	potatoes, cooked, mashed and cooled	1 cup
225g/8oz	canned tuna fish, drained and flaked	1^{1}/$_{3}$ cups
15g/^{1}/$_{2}$oz	fresh parsley, chopped	^{1}/$_{2}$ cup
1 small	lemon, zest of	1 small
2	eggs, lightly beaten	2
1 tbsp	wholemeal flour	1 tbsp
55g/2oz	dried wholemeal breadcrumbs	^{1}/$_{2}$ cup
1 tbsp	sunflower oil	1 tbsp

1. Put the cold mashed potato into a large mixing bowl.
2. Add the tuna fish, parsley, lemon zest and half the egg, and fold the mixture together.
3. Shape the mixture into 8 fishcakes and coat with the flour.
4. Dip each cake in the remaining egg and coat with the breadcrumbs.
5. Heat the oil in a shallow non-stick frying pan. Cook the fishcakes over a moderate heat for 3 minutes on each side. Drain thoroughly on kitchen paper.
6. Serve hot with freshly cooked vegetables or cold with a salad.

Note to Cooks

Can be frozen at stages 4 or 5.

Anaemia

BROCCOLI AND CHEESE FLAN

Fe	Fol	B$_{12}$
2.4	85	1.13

Serves 4

Metric/Imperial		*American*
225g/8oz	shortcrust pastry	1/2 lb
225g/8oz	broccoli, divided into florets	1/2 lb
2	eggs, beaten	2
140ml/1/4 pint	milk	2/3 cup
1 tsp	mustard powder	1 tsp
115g/4oz	Cheddar cheese, grated	1 cup

1. Roll out the pastry and use to line a 20cm/8-inch flan tin.
2. Pierce the pastry all over with a fork. Cover with lightly greased greaseproof paper, fill with dried beans and bake blind in a preheated oven at 200°C/400°F/gas mark 6 for 10 minutes. Remove the paper and beans.
3. Cook the broccoli until tender, drain well and chop roughly, then arrange evenly in the flan case.
4. Combine the eggs and milk, then add the mustard and most of the cheese.
5. Pour the egg mixture over the broccoli and sprinkle with the remaining cheese.
6. Bake in a preheated oven at 180°C/350°F/gas mark 4 for 30–35 minutes. Serve hot or cold.

Note to Cooks

Can be frozen.

CHEESE AND MUSHROOM TOASTS

Fe	Fol	B$_{12}$
2.7	51	0.40

Serves 4

Metric/Imperial		*American*
45g/1½oz	polyunsaturated margarine	3 tbsp
1 small	onion, finely chopped	1 small
115g/4oz	mushrooms, thinly sliced	2 cups
2 tbsp	chopped fresh parsley	2 tbsp
1 tsp	lemon juice	1 tsp
30g/1oz	flour	¼ cup
140ml/¼ pint	milk	⅔ cup
	freshly grated nutmeg	
55g/2oz	Parmesan cheese, grated	½ cup
8 slices	wholemeal bread	8 slices

1. Melt 1 tablespoon of the margarine in a non-stick shallow frying pan. Add the onion and fry over a gentle heat until softened.

2. Add the mushrooms, parsley and lemon juice. Cover and simmer for 10 minutes.

3. Melt the remaining margarine in a non-stick saucepan. Add the flour and stir over gentle heat. Add the milk gradually, bring to the boil and cook over a moderate heat for at least 3 minutes.

4. Stir in the nutmeg and three-quarters of the Parmesan cheese. Leave the mixture to cool.

5. Arrange the bread in a shallow baking tin. Spread with the mixture and sprinkle with the remaining cheese.

Anaemia

6. Bake in a preheated oven at 200°C/400°F/gas mark 6 for 20 minutes.
7. Serve immediately with a green salad.

CHEESE AND SAGE SAUSAGES

Fe	Fol	B$_{12}$
1.5	42	0.98

Serves 4

Metric/Imperial		*American*
115g/4oz	Cheddar cheese, grated	1 cup
140g/5oz	fresh white breadcrumbs	2¹/₂ cups
1 small	onion, finely chopped	1 small
2 heaped tbsp	chopped fresh sage	2 heaped tbsp
	freshly ground black pepper	
2	eggs, lightly beaten	2
30g/1oz	dried wholemeal breadcrumbs	¹/₄ cup
1 tbsp	sunflower oil	1 tbsp

1. Put the cheese, fresh breadcrumbs and onion into a large mixing bowl.
2. Add the sage, pepper and half the beaten egg; stir thoroughly.
3. Shape the mixture into 16 small sausage shapes. Dip them into the remaining beaten egg and coat evenly with the dried breadcrumbs.
4. Heat the oil in a shallow non-stick frying pan. Fry the sausages over a moderate heat for 5 minutes. Turn to ensure even cooking.
5. Drain the sausages on kitchen paper.
6. Serve hot or cold with a mixed salad.

Note to Cooks

Can be frozen.

CHEESE AND VEGETABLE LOAF

Fe	Fol	B$_{12}$
1.3	65	0.57

Serves 4

Metric/Imperial		*American*
1 tbsp	sunflower oil	1 tbsp
1 small	onion, finely chopped	1 small
115g/4oz	mushrooms, finely chopped	2 cups
1 medium	green pepper, seeded and diced	1 medium
1 medium	red pepper, seeded and diced	1 medium
1 medium stick	celery, finely chopped	1 medium stalk
115g/4oz	fresh white breadcrumbs	2 cups
85g/3oz	Cheddar cheese, grated	3/4 cup
1	egg	1
2 tbsp	chopped fresh parsley	2 tbsp

1. Heat the oil in a shallow non-stick frying pan, add the onion and fry over a gentle heat until softened.
2. Add the mushrooms, peppers and celery and continue cooking for a further 5 minutes.
3. Turn off the heat and add the breadcrumbs, cheese, egg and parsley. Mix well.
4. Pour the mixture into a non-stick or lightly greased and lined loaf tin and spread evenly.
5. Bake in a preheated oven at 190°C/375°F/gas mark 5 for 1 hour.

6. Leave the mixture in the tin for about 15 minutes to allow it to settle; then carefully turn out onto a serving dish.
7. Serve hot with jacket potatoes and a variety of salads – or with a mixture of vegetables and a well-flavoured tomato sauce.

BROCCOLI SOUFFLÉ

Serves 4

	Fe	Fol	B$_{12}$
	2.8	108	1.42

Metric/Imperial		*American*
340g/³/₄ lb	broccoli	³/₄ lb
30g/1oz	butter	2 tbsp
30g/1oz	plain flour	¹/₄ cup
140ml/¹/₄ pint	milk	²/₃ cup
4	eggs, separated	4

1. Cook the broccoli in boiling water for 10 minutes and drain thoroughly.
2. Put the broccoli in a liquidizer or food processor and process until smooth.
3. Melt the butter in a saucepan, add the flour and stir until thoroughly mixed.
4. Add the milk gradually, stirring continuously to prevent any lumps from forming.
5. Bring the mixture to boiling point and continue stirring until the sauce is thick.
6. Add the egg yolks to the sauce, then add the broccoli purée. Stir well.
7. Whisk the egg whites until stiff, then gently fold into the broccoli mixture.
8. Lightly grease a 1.1 litre/2 pint soufflé dish and pour in the broccoli mixture.
9. Bake in a preheated oven at 180°C/350°F/gas mark 4 for 1 hour.
10. Serve at once.

CURRIED EGGS

Serves 4

	Fe	Fol	B$_{12}$
	1.7	31	0.62

Metric/Imperial		American
4	eggs	4
15g/½oz	margarine	1 tbsp
1 large	onion, finely sliced	1 large
2 large	garlic cloves, crushed	2 large
1 tsp	ground coriander	1 tsp
1 tsp	ground ginger	1 tsp
½ tsp	chilli powder	½ tsp
½ tsp	garam masala	½ tsp
pinch of	ground cumin	pinch of
140ml/¼ pint	natural (plain) yogurt	⅔ cup
2	cloves	2
6	peppercorns	6

1. Hardboil the eggs, shell and cut in half lengthways. Arrange in a shallow dish, cut-side down.
2. Heat the fat in a heavy saucepan, add the onion and garlic and fry over moderate heat until the onion browns.
3. Add the coriander, ginger, chilli powder, garam masala and cumin and continue frying for another 5 minutes.
4. Add the yogurt, cloves and peppercorns and continue cooking for 3 minutes.
5. Pour the mixture over the eggs and serve with rice or chapatis and sambals.

SALMON FRITTATA

Serves 4

Fe	Fol	B$_{12}$
1.7	49	1.42

Metric/Imperial		*American*
115g/4oz	smoked salmon	1/4 lb
1 tbsp	sunflower oil	1 tbsp
1 small	onion, finely chopped	1 small
2	spring onions, finely chopped	2
1 small	green pepper, seeded and chopped	1 small
1 medium	tomato, seeded and chopped	1 medium
4	eggs	4
140ml/1/4 pint	milk	2/3 cup
	freshly ground black pepper	

1. Chop the smoked salmon into uniform-size pieces.
2. Heat the oil in a medium-sized frying pan and add the onion, spring onions and pepper and cook for 3 minutes.
3. Add the tomato and continue to cook for 1 minute. Leave to cool for about 10 minutes.
4. Beat the eggs with the milk and add the pepper.
5. Combine the egg mixture with the vegetables and salmon, and pour into a greased ovenproof 20cm/8-inch flan dish.
6. Bake in a preheated oven at 180°C/350°F/gas mark 4 for about 20–25 minutes.
7. Serve hot cut in wedges with a green salad.

HERBY LENTIL SALAD

Serves 4

	Fe	Fol	B$_{12}$
	6.6	69	0

Metric/Imperial		*American*
225g/8oz	brown lentils	1 cup
2 large	garlic cloves, crushed	2 large
4 tbsp	chopped fresh chives	4 tbsp
4 tbsp	chopped fresh parsley	4 tbsp
2 tbsp	French dressing	2 tbsp
2	spring onions, finely chopped	2

1. Put the lentils in a large pan with enough water to cover. Bring to boiling point, then simmer for 30 minutes and drain thoroughly.
2. Put the hot lentils in a large mixing bowl. Add the garlic, chives, parsley and French dressing. Lightly stir until thoroughly combined.
3. Leave the mixture to cool, during which time the lentils will absorb all the flavours.
4. Chill for 1 hour, then serve sprinkled with the onions.

LENTIL BURGERS

Serves 4

Fe	Fol	B$_{12}$
3.9	46	0.64

Metric/Imperial		*American*
115g/4oz	split red lentils	½ cup
55g/2oz	mushrooms, finely chopped	1 cup
1 medium	carrot, grated	1 medium
2 tbsp	chopped fresh sage	2 tbsp
55g/2oz	fresh wholemeal breadcrumbs	1 cup
2	eggs, lightly beaten	2
1 tbsp	wholemeal flour	1 tbsp
55g/2oz	dried wholemeal breadcrumbs	½ cup
1 tbsp	sunflower oil	1 tbsp

1. Boil the lentils in 570ml/1 pint of water for about 20 minutes. Drain thoroughly.
2. Put the lentils, mushrooms, carrot, sage, fresh breadcrumbs and half the eggs in a mixing bowl and stir well.
3. Shape the mixture into 8 burgers and coat with the flour.
4. Dip the burgers in the remaining egg and coat thoroughly with the dried breadcrumbs.
5. Heat the oil in a shallow non-stick frying pan. Cook the burgers for 5 minutes on each side. Drain on kitchen paper.
6. Serve hot with fresh vegetables or cold with a selection of salads.

Note to Cooks

Can be frozen.

VEGETABLE 'HOT' POT

Serves 4

Fe	Fol	B$_{12}$
2.8	56	0

Metric/Imperial		American
1 tbsp	sunflower oil	1 tbsp
4	garlic cloves, crushed	4
1 large	onion, sliced	1 large
1 small	red chilli, seeded and diced	1 small
2 medium	carrots, diced	2 medium
2 medium	red peppers, seeded and diced	2 medium
455g/1 lb	canned, chopped tomatoes	2¹/₄ cups
1 tbsp	tomato purée	1 tbsp
¹/₄ tsp	ground cumin	¹/₄ tsp
285g/10oz	drained canned red kidney beans	1¹/₂ cups
85g/3oz	mushrooms, sliced	1¹/₂ cups
4 tbsp	chopped fresh parsley	4 tbsp

1. Heat the oil in a flameproof casserole. Add the garlic, onion and chilli. Cook over a gentle heat for 10 minutes.
2. Add the carrots, peppers, tomatoes, tomato purée and cumin. Bring to the boil, cover and simmer for 15 minutes.
3. Add the beans and mushrooms and cook for a further 5 minutes.
4. Sprinkle with the parsley and serve hot with crusty garlic bread or jacket potatoes.

SMOKED TOFU STIR-FRY

Serves 4

Fe	Fol	B$_{12}$
2.4	54	0

Metric/Imperial		*American*
6	spring onions	6
1 medium	carrot	1 medium
1 medium	green pepper, seeded	1 medium
1 medium	red pepper, seeded	1 medium
225g/8oz	firm smoked tofu	½ lb
1 tbsp	sunflower oil	1 tbsp
115g/4oz	button mushrooms	2 cups
4 tbsp	soya sauce	4 tbsp

1. Trim and cut the spring onions into strips about 2.5 cm/1 inch long.
2. Cut the carrot into matchstick-size pieces.
3. Slice the peppers into 1 x 2.5 cm/½ x 1 inch pieces.
4. Cut the tofu into 2.5 cm/1 inch cubes.
5. Heat the oil in a heavy shallow frying pan or wok.
6. Add the vegetables and cook over moderate heat for 3 minutes, stirring constantly.
7. Add the tofu and soy sauce and continue cooking for a further 2 minutes.
8. Serve immediately accompanied by Veggie Rice (page 133).

ALMOND RICE

Serves 4

	Fe	Fol	B$_{12}$
	2.4	68	0

Metric/Imperial   *American*

Metric/Imperial		American
1 tbsp	sunflower oil	1 tbsp
1	garlic clove, crushed	1
1 medium	onion, chopped	1 medium
1 tbsp	chopped fresh ginger root	1 tbsp
1 medium	red pepper, seeded and diced	1 medium
115g/4oz	mushrooms, sliced	2 cups
2 sticks	celery, chopped	2 stalks
55g/2oz	sultanas	1/3 cup
1 tsp	ground coriander	1 tsp
200g/7oz	brown rice	1 cup
570ml/1 pint	hot vegetable stock	2 1/2 cups
115g/4oz	flaked almonds, toasted	1 cup

1. Heat the oil in a heavy pan. Add the garlic, onion and ginger and fry over a moderate heat for 5 minutes.
2. Add the pepper, mushrooms, celery and sultanas and continue cooking for 3 more minutes.
3. Add the coriander and rice and stir well.
4. Add the hot stock, cover and simmer over a gentle heat for about 40 minutes or until the rice is thoroughly cooked.
5. Spoon the rice onto a hot serving dish, sprinkle with the toasted almonds and serve immediately.

PEANUT BAKE

Fe	Fol	B$_{12}$
3.6	110	0.64

Serves 4

Metric/Imperial		American
1 tbsp	sunflower oil	1 tbsp
1 small	onion, finely chopped	1 small
2	carrots, finely chopped	2
2 medium sticks	celery, finely chopped	2 medium stalks
225g/8oz	mushrooms, finely chopped	4 cups
170g/6oz	fresh wholemeal breadcrumbs	3 cups
170g/6oz	peanuts, finely chopped	1¹⁄₃ cups
1 tsp	dried mixed herbs	1 tsp
2 tbsp	soya sauce	2 tbsp
2	eggs, beaten	2

1. Heat the oil in a shallow frying pan and fry the onion over a gentle heat until softened.
2. Add the carrot, celery and mushrooms and continue cooking for 3 more minutes.
3. Tip the fried vegetables into a mixing bowl and add the breadcrumbs, peanuts, herbs, soya sauce and eggs and mix well.
4. Pour the mixture into a non-stick or lightly greased and lined 1.1 litre/2 pint loaf tin. Smooth the top using a palette knife.
5. Bake in a preheated oven at 190°C/375°F/gas mark 5 for 40–45 minutes.

Main Protein Dishes

6. Leave the dish to stand for at least 15 minutes before turning it out of the tin.
7. Serve hot or cold with a mixed salad or a selection of vegetables.

8

Vegetables and Salads

BROCCOLI WITH ALMONDS

Fe	Fol	B$_{12}$
2.4	109	0

Serves 4

Metric/Imperial		American
455g/1 lb	broccoli, separated into florets	1 lb
15g/½ oz	butter	1 tbsp
55g/2oz	flaked almonds	½ cup
1 tsp	lemon juice	1 tsp

1. Cook the broccoli in boiling water or in a microwave oven until barely tender. Drain well.
2. Heat the butter in a saucepan and fry the almonds over a gentle heat until golden brown. Add the lemon juice and mix thoroughly.
3. Arrange the cooked broccoli in a hot serving dish and pour the almond mixture over the top. Serve immediately.

BRUSSELS SPROUTS WITH ONION AND BACON

Fe	Fol	B$_{12}$
1.1	164	0

Serves 4

Metric/Imperial		*American*
680g/1½ lb	Brussels sprouts	1½ lb
4 rashers	rindless streaky bacon, diced	4 slices
1 large	onion, finely sliced	1 large

1. Cook the sprouts until barely tender. Drain well.
2. Fry the bacon in a shallow non-stick frying pan over a moderate heat for 5 minutes.
3. Add the onion and continue cooking for a further 5 minutes.
4. Add the sprouts to the pan and toss the mixture over a gentle heat for 2 minutes. Serve at once.

BUBBLE AND SQUEAK

Serves 4

Fe	Fol	B$_{12}$
0.5	35	0

Metric/Imperial		*American*
225g/8oz	cooked cabbage	½ lb
225g/8oz	mashed potatoes	1 cup
115g/4oz	mashed cooked carrots	½ cup
30g/1oz	butter	2 tbsp
	freshly ground black pepper	

1. Mix the cabbage, potatoes and carrots together in a mixing bowl.
2. Melt half the butter in a shallow non-stick frying pan over a gentle heat.
3. Tip the cabbage mixture into the pan and flatten it using a palette knife. Cook over a gentle heat for 10 minutes.
4. Put a plate over the top of the pan and invert the pan so that the mixture falls neatly onto the plate.
5. Melt the remaining butter in the pan. Slide the vegetable mixture back into the pan and cook for a further 10 minutes.
6. Slip the bubble and squeak onto a hot serving plate and season generously with black pepper.

CABBAGE CASSEROLE

Serves 4

	Fe	Fol	B$_{12}$
	1.0	94	0

Metric/Imperial		*American*
455g/1 lb	green cabbage	1 lb
1 medium	onion, finely sliced	1 medium
2 medium	carrots, chopped	2 medium
2 sticks	celery, chopped	2 stalks
285ml/½ pint	hot vegetable stock	1⅓ cups
1	bouquet garni	1

1. Cut the cabbage into quarters. Discard any discoloured leaves and remove the stalk. Wash the cabbage under cold running water and drain thoroughly.
2. Put the onion, carrots and celery into a large oven-proof casserole. Place the cabbage on top.
3. Add the hot vegetable stock and the bouquet garni, cover and cook in a preheated oven at 190°C/375°F/ gas mark 5 for 12 minutes.

CORIANDER CARROTS

Serves 4

Fe	Fol	B_{12}
0.7	48	0

Metric/Imperial		*American*
680g/1½ lb	young carrots	1½ lb
15g/½oz	butter	1 tbsp
2 tbsp	finely chopped fresh coriander	2 tbsp

1. Scrape the carrots if necessary. Cook until tender and drain well.
2. Put the butter and coriander into a saucepan over a gentle heat and lightly toss the cooked carrots in the mixture until they are coated.
3. Serve immediately.

ROMAN-STYLE BEANS

Serves 4

Fe	Fol	B$_{12}$
1.6	96	0.33

Metric/Imperial		*American*
455g/1 lb	French beans	1 lb
15g/½oz	butter	1 tbsp
1	onion, finely chopped	1
1	garlic clove, crushed	1
4	canned anchovies, chopped	4

1. Cook the beans for 7 minutes in just enough water to cover. Drain well.
2. Melt the butter over a gentle heat in a shallow non-stick frying pan. Add the onion and garlic and fry over a low heat for 5 minutes.
3. Add the beans and anchovies and stir thoroughly. Cook for 1 minute and serve hot.

THREE-ROOT PURÉE

Serves 4

Fe	Fol	B$_{12}$
0.4	30	0.14

Metric/Imperial		*American*
225g/8oz	potatoes, chopped	½ lb
225g/8oz	swede, chopped	½ lb
225g/8oz	carrots, sliced	½ lb
15g/½oz	butter	1 tbsp
140ml/¼ pint	milk	⅔ cup
	freshly grated nutmeg	

1. Cook the vegetables in a large pan of boiling water until tender. Drain thoroughly and return to the pan.
2. Add the butter, milk and nutmeg and mash, using a potato masher.
3. Reheat the purée over gentle heat, then pile the mixture into a hot serving dish.

VEGETABLE STIR-FRY

Serves 4

Fe	Fol	B₁₂
0.9	48	0

Metric/Imperial		American
115g/4oz	cauliflower, broken into florets	1 cup
1 tbsp	sunflower oil	1 tbsp
1 medium	carrot, cut into matchstick strips	1 medium
1 small	onion, sliced	1 small
115g/4oz	mushrooms, sliced	2 cups
1 medium	green pepper, seeded and sliced	1 medium
2 tbsp	soya sauce	2 tbsp

1. Blanch the cauliflower florets by cooking in boiling water for 1 minute then plunging into cold water. Drain thoroughly.
2. Heat the oil in a wok or shallow frying pan.
3. Add the vegetables and stir-fry for 5 minutes.
4. Stir in the soya sauce and serve at once.

SAVOURY APPLE AND BANANA SALAD

	Fe	Fol	B$_{12}$
	0.4	21	0.07

Serves 4

Metric/Imperial		*American*
4 sticks	celery	4 stalks
2 medium	bananas	2 medium
1 tbsp	lemon juice	1 tbsp
2 medium	eating apples	2 medium
1 small	onion, finely chopped	1 small
1 small	lime, zest and juice	1 small
140ml/¼ pint	natural (plain) yogurt	²/₃ cup

1. Cut the celery into 5 mm/¼ inch pieces.
2. Cut the bananas into 5 mm/¼ inch pieces and lightly brush with half the lemon juice.
3. Core and slice the apples and brush with the remaining lemon juice.
4. Put all the ingredients in a large mixing bowl and gently mix together.
5. Chill for 30 minutes before serving.

AVOCADO SALAD WITH
ROQUEFORT CHEESE

Fe	Fol	B$_{12}$
0.7	34	0.12

Serves 4

Metric/Imperial   *American*

1 medium	avocado pear	1 medium
1 tsp	lemon juice	1 tsp
1	cos lettuce, shredded	1
55g/2oz	watercress, trimmed	2 cups
115g/4oz	Roquefort cheese, crumbled	1/4 lb

1. Peel, stone and dice the avocado pear, then gently brush with lemon juice.
2. Mix all the ingredients together in a large bowl and serve chilled.

BEETROOT AND PEPPER SALAD

Fe	Fol	B$_{12}$
0.9	96	0

Serves 4

Metric/Imperial		*American*
225g/8oz	cooked beetroot	1/2 lb
1 medium	green pepper, seeded	1 medium
1 medium	red pepper, seeded	1 medium
1 medium	yellow pepper, seeded	1 medium
140ml/1/4 pint	French dressing	2/3 cup

1. Cut the beetroot into 5 mm/1/4 inch strips.
2. Cut the peppers into 5 mm/1/4 inch strips.
3. Mix the beetroot and peppers with the French dressing in a large mixing bowl.
4. Serve chilled.

CAULIFLOWER NEAPOLITAN

Serves 4

Fe	Fol	B$_{12}$
1.0	82	0

Metric/Imperial		*American*
455g/1 lb	cauliflower, broken into florets	1 lb
1 small	onion, finely chopped	1 small
2 sticks	celery, finely chopped	2 stalks
10	stuffed green olives, sliced	10
6 tbsp	olive oil	6 tbsp
2 tbsp	lemon juice	2 tbsp
6	capers	6
2 tbsp	chopped fresh parsley	2 tbsp
	freshly ground black pepper	

1. Cook the cauliflower florets in boiling water for 5 minutes. Drain well.
2. Combine the remaining ingredients together in a small mixing bowl.
3. Put the cauliflower florets in a serving dish, pour on the dressing and toss lightly.
4. Serve chilled.

GREEN SALAD WITH BASIL

Fe	Fol	B$_{12}$
1.2	19	0

Serves 4

Metric/Imperial		*American*
1	cos lettuce, shredded	1
55g/2oz	fresh basil leaves	2 cups
30g/1oz	watercress, trimmed	1 cup
1/2	cucumber, thinly sliced	1/2

1. Put all the ingredients together in a serving dish and toss gently.
2. Serve at once.

NUT COLESLAW

Serves 4

Fe	Fol	B$_{12}$
0.6	36	0.09

Metric/Imperial		*American*
225g/8oz	white cabbage, shredded	1/2 lb
2 medium	carrots, coarsely grated	2 medium
1 small	onion, finely sliced	1 small
55g/2oz	roasted salted peanuts	3 1/2 tbsp
60ml/2fl oz	mayonnaise	1/4 cup

1. Rinse the cabbage quickly under cold running water. Drain thoroughly.
2. Put all the ingredients in a large mixing bowl. Stir gently until thoroughly mixed together.
3. Chill for 30 minutes before serving.

TANGY LEEK SALAD

Serves 4

Fe	Fol	B$_{12}$
0.9	37	0

Metric/Imperial		American
4 small	leeks	4 small
2 medium	oranges, zest and juice	2 medium
2 tbsp	chopped fresh tarragon	2 tbsp
1 tbsp	olive oil	1 tbsp
30g/1oz	watercress, trimmed	1/2 cup

1. Cut the leeks diagonally into 1 cm/1/2 inch pieces.
2. Cook until just tender by boiling or in a microwave oven. Drain well and leave to cool.
3. Put the leeks, orange zest and juice, tarragon and olive oil into a mixing bowl and toss together gently until thoroughly mixed.
4. Chill for 30 minutes, and serve garnished with the watercress.

TOMATO AND MINT SALAD

Serves 4

Fe	Fol	B$_{12}$
0.9	30	0

Metric/Imperial		*American*
8 medium	tomatoes, skinned, seeded and chopped	8 medium
4	shallots, finely chopped	4
4 tbsp	chopped fresh mint	4 tbsp
1 tbsp	French dressing	1 tbsp
4	fresh mint sprigs	4

1. Put the tomatoes, shallots, mint and dressing into a serving dish. Fold the ingredients together gently and chill for 30 minutes.
2. Garnish with the sprigs of fresh mint.

9

Potatoes and Grains

CAULIFLOWER AND POTATO BAKE

Fe	Fol	B$_{12}$
0.8	73	0.26

Serves 4

Metric/Imperial		*American*
455g/1 lb	new potatoes, sliced	1 lb
225g/8oz	cauliflower, broken into florets	1/2 lb
2 large	garlic cloves, crushed	2 large
140ml/1/4 pint	single cream	2/3 cup
55g/2oz	Cheddar cheese, grated	1/2 cup

1. Cook the potatoes in boiling water for 5 minutes and drain well.
2. Layer the potatoes and cauliflower florets in a non-stick or lightly buttered shallow ovenproof serving dish.
3. Stir the garlic into the cream and pour over the layered vegetables.
4. Sprinkle with the cheese, cover with foil and cook in a

preheated oven at 180°C/350°F/gas mark 4 for 50 minutes.

5. Remove from the oven and put under a preheated hot grill until golden brown.

6. Serve immediately.

EMMENTAL POTATOES

Serves 4

Fe	Fol	B$_{12}$
0.9	79	0.85

Metric/Imperial		*American*
900g/2 lb	potatoes	2 lb
115g/4oz	Emmental cheese, grated	1 cup
30g/1oz	butter	2 tbsp
4 slices	Emmental cheese	4 slices

1. Boil the potatoes in their skins. Drain well.
2. Peel and coarsely grate the potatoes into a mixing bowl and add the grated cheese.
3. Melt half the butter in a shallow non-stick frying pan over a gentle heat.
4. Add the potato mixture and flatten the surface with a palette knife. Cook over a gentle heat for 10 minutes.
5. Put a plate over the top of the pan and invert the pan so that the potato mixture falls neatly onto the plate.
6. Melt the remaining butter in the pan, then slide the potato mixture back into the pan. Cook for a further 10 minutes.
7. Slip the pancake shape onto a hot serving plate and arrange the slices of cheese on top.
8. This dish goes well with mixed grill and salad.

MINTED POTATO SALAD

Serves 4

Fe	Fol	B$_{12}$
1.1	43	0.07

Metric/Imperial		*American*
455g/1 lb	baby new potatoes	1 lb
1	eating apple	1
1 tsp	lemon juice	1 tsp
30g/1oz	fresh mint leaves, finely chopped	1 cup
140ml/¼ pint	natural set yogurt	⅔ cup
4	fresh mint sprigs	4

1. Boil the potatoes until tender. Drain and leave to cool.
2. Peel, core and chop the apple then brush it with the lemon juice.
3. Put the cooked potatoes into a large mixing bowl and very roughly cut up into chunks. Add the apple, chopped mint leaves and yogurt and fold the mixture together.
4. Chill for 30 minutes to allow the flavours to blend.
5. Serve piled up in a serving dish garnished with the sprigs of mint.

POTATO AND GARLIC CAKES

Serves 4

Fe	Fol	B$_{12}$
1.6	53	0.64

Metric/Imperial		*American*
1	garlic bulb, separated into cloves	1
455g/1 lb	potatoes	1 lb
2	eggs, beaten	2
1 tbsp	plain flour	1 tbsp
55g/2oz	dried breadcrumbs	1/2 cup
2 tbsp	sunflower oil	2 tbsp

1. Peel the garlic cloves and place in a pan with enough water to cover. Cover and simmer for 30 minutes. Drain and set aside.
2. Cut the potatoes into uniform-size pieces. Boil until tender then drain well.
3. Pass the potatoes and garlic through a mouli grater or potato ricer into a mixing bowl.
4. Add a quarter of the beaten egg and mix well with a wooden spoon.
5. Turn the potato mixture onto a lightly floured work surface and shape into 12 rounds.
6. Coat with the remaining egg and the breadcrumbs. Chill for 30 minutes.
7. Heat the oil in a shallow non-stick frying pan and fry the cakes for 5 minutes on each side over a moderate heat. Serve hot.

POTATO SKINS WITH SPINACH FILLING

Fe	Fol	B_{12}
2.3	120	0.03

Serves 4

Metric/Imperial		*American*
4 medium	potatoes	4 medium
2 tbsp	sunflower oil	2 tbsp
2 large	garlic cloves, crushed	2 large
225g/8oz	frozen spinach, thawed and drained	½ lb
2 tbsp	natural yogurt	2 tbsp
55g/2oz	fresh brown breadcrumbs	1 cup

1. Score the potato skins all round with the point of a sharp knife.
2. Bake until tender in a preheated oven at 200°C/400°F/ gas mark 6.
3. Cut the cooked potatoes into quarters and scoop out the flesh leaving a 5-mm/¼-inch shell. Reserve the flesh.
4. Brush the potato skins all over with half the oil and bake in the oven for 10 minutes.
5. Heat the remaining oil in a shallow frying pan and add the garlic. Cook over a gentle heat for 2 minutes.
6. Add the spinach to the pan, increase the heat and cook until any excess moisture has evaporated. Remove from the heat and stir in the reserved potato flesh, yogurt and half the breadcrumbs.

7. Spoon the mixture into the prepared potato skins, sprinkle with the remaining breadcrumbs and bake for 10–12 minutes.
8. Serve at once.

SWISS-STYLE POTATO GRATIN

Fe	Fol	B_{12}
0.9	69	0.55

Serves 4

Metric/Imperial		*American*
900g/2 lb	potatoes, thinly sliced	2 lb
4 large	garlic cloves, crushed	4 large
	freshly ground black pepper	
15g/½oz	butter	1 tbsp
115g/4oz	Gruyère cheese, grated	1 cup
6 tbsp	milk	6 tbsp

1. Put the potatoes in a large bowl, add the garlic and pepper and mix together.
2. Grease a gratin dish with the butter.
3. Layer the seasoned potatoes with the cheese, ending with a topping of cheese.
4. Pour on the milk, cover with foil and bake in a preheated oven at 180°C/350°F/gas mark 4 for 45 minutes.
5. Remove the foil and continue cooking for a further 15 minutes until the surface is golden brown.

BULGAR WHEAT SALAD

Serves 4

	Fe	Fol	B$_{12}$
	4.9	56	0

Metric/Imperial		*American*
170g/6oz	bulgar wheat	1 cup
1 tbsp	lemon juice	1 tbsp
2 tbsp	olive oil	2 tbsp
	freshly ground black pepper	
225g/8oz	tomatoes, skinned, seeded and roughly chopped	1/2 lb
10	spring onions, chopped	10
55g/2oz	chopped fresh mint	2 cups
30g/1oz	chopped fresh parsley	1 cup

1. Put the bulgar wheat in a large bowl. Add enough cold water to cover then leave to stand for 1 hour.
2. Combine the lemon juice with the olive oil and pepper.
3. Drain any excess liquid from the bulgar wheat and tip the grains into a large mixing bowl.
4. Add the tomatoes, spring onions, dressing and chopped mint.
5. Chill for 30 minutes and serve garnished with the parsley.

FRUIT AND RICE SALAD

Serves 4

Fe	Fol	B_{12}
0.7	46	0

Metric/Imperial		*American*
225g/8oz	Patna rice	8oz
140g/5oz	fresh pineapple, chopped	1 cup
2	oranges	2
2	eating apples	2
1 tbsp	lemon juice	1 tbsp
2	bananas	2
2 tbsp	chopped fresh parsley	2 tbsp

1. Cook the rice according to the instructions on the packet. Leave to cool.
2. Put the rice in a large mixing bowl and add the pineapple chunks.
3. Peel the oranges and segment them, holding the fruit over the rice mixture to capture the juice. Put the segments into the bowl.
4. Peel, core and chop the apples. Brush with half the lemon juice and add to the rice mixture.
5. Peel and slice the bananas. Brush with the remaining lemon juice and add to the other ingredients.
6. Fold the mixture together and chill for 30 minutes before serving.
7. Serve sprinkled with the chopped parsley.

SAVOURY PASTA

Serves 4

	Fe	Fol	B$_{12}$
	1.8	28	0.26

Metric/Imperial		*American*
1 tbsp	sunflower oil	1 tbsp
2 medium	onions, finely chopped	2 medium
4 large	garlic cloves, crushed	4 large
30g/1oz	fresh basil leaves, chopped	1 cup
2 tbsp	tomato purée	2 tbsp
225g/8oz	pasta shells	4 cups
55g/2oz	Parmesan cheese, grated	1/2 cup

1. Heat the oil in a non-stick pan. Add the onions and garlic and fry over a gentle heat to soften the onions.
2. Stir in the basil and tomato purée, then set aside.
3. Cook the pasta according to packet instructions. Drain thoroughly and stir into the onion mixture.
4. Heat gently for 2 minutes, then serve in a hot dish sprinkled with the Parmesan cheese.
5. This dish goes well with grilled meat – especially kebabs.

TOMATO RISOTTO

Serves 4

	Fe	Fol	B$_{12}$
	1.4	43	0.55

Metric/Imperial   *American*

1 tbsp	sunflower oil	1 tbsp
1 small	onion, finely chopped	1 small
2	garlic cloves, crushed	2
225g/8oz	risotto rice	1/2 lb
455g/1 lb	tomatoes, skinned, seeded and chopped	1 lb
2 tbsp	tomato purée	2 tbsp
1 litre/1³/4 pints	hot vegetable stock	4¹/2 cups
30g/1oz	butter	2 tbsp
115g/4oz	Parmesan cheese, grated	1 cup

1. Heat the oil in a flameproof casserole, and fry the onion and garlic over a gentle heat until softened.
2. Add the rice and cook until translucent.
3. Add the tomatoes, tomato purée and hot stock. Cover and cook for 25–30 minutes until all the liquid is absorbed.
4. Stir in the butter and Parmesan cheese and serve immediately.
5. This dish goes well with meat and fish dishes.

VEGGIE RICE

Serves 4

	Fe	Fol	B$_{12}$
	1.1	46	0

Metric/Imperial		*American*
1 tbsp	olive oil	1 tbsp
225g/8oz	brown rice	1 cup
570ml/1 pint	vegetable stock	2½ cups
85g/3oz	carrots, diced	⅓ cup
55g/2oz	frozen sweetcorn kernels, thawed	⅓ cup
55g/2oz	French beans, sliced	⅓ cup
1 tbsp	chopped fresh oregano	1 tbsp

1. Heat the oil in a heavy pan, add the rice and fry over a moderate heat until translucent.
2. Add the vegetable stock, bring to the boil, cover and simmer for 30 minutes.
3. Add the vegetables and continue cooking for another 10 minutes.
4. Pile the rice onto a hot serving dish and sprinkle with the chopped oregano.

10

Sweet Dishes

BREAD PUDDING

Serves 4

	Fe	Fol	B$_{12}$
	2.7	32	0.29

Metric/Imperial		*American*
225g/8oz	fresh wholemeal breadcrumbs	4 cups
285ml/½ pint	milk	1⅓ cups
30g/1oz	butter	2 tbsp
55g/2oz	soft brown sugar	⅓ cup
2 tsp	ground mixed spice	2 tsp
55g/2oz	currants	⅓ cup
55g/2oz	seedless raisins	⅓ cup
55g/2oz	sultanas	⅓ cup
30g/1oz	candied peel	1 tbsp
1	orange, grated zest	1

1. Tip the breadcrumbs into a mixing bowl and add the milk. Cover and leave to stand for 1 hour.
2. Melt the butter in a pan then add to the milk mixture with the sugar and mixed spice.

3. Beat the mixture using a fork, then stir in the currants, raisins, sultanas, candied peel and orange zest.
4. Spread the mixture in a lightly greased shallow baking dish and bake in a preheated oven at 180°C/ 350°F/gas mark 4 for 1 hour or until set.
5. Serve hot as a dessert or cold as a cake.

BROWN BREAD ICECREAM

Serves 4

	Fe	Fol	B$_{12}$
	1.4	30	0.85

Metric/Imperial		*American*
85g/3oz	fresh brown breadcrumbs	½ cup
85g/3oz	brown sugar	½ cup
425ml/¾ pint	double cream	2 cups
2	eggs, separated	2

1. Mix the breadcrumbs and sugar together and spread evenly on a baking tray. Bake in a preheated oven at 190°C/375°F/gas mark 5 for 10 minutes. Leave to cool.
2. Whip the cream. Whisk the egg whites until light and fluffy. Lightly beat the egg yolks.
3. Fold the egg yolks and caramelised breadcrumbs into the cream, then fold in the egg whites.
4. Spread the mixture in a shallow container suitable for freezing (eg a Swiss roll tin) and freeze for 3 hours.
5. Remove from the freezer 20 minutes before serving and put in the refrigerator.

CHOCOLATE AND ORANGE DESSERT

Fe	Fol	B$_{12}$
2.4	64	0.96

Serves 4

Metric/Imperial		*American*
2	oranges	2
170g/6oz	unsalted butter, chilled	¾ cup
225g/8oz	plain chocolate	½ lb
1 tbsp	strong black coffee	1 tbsp
3	eggs, separated	3
115g/4oz	icing sugar	⅔ cup
12	fresh mint leaves	12

1. Remove the zest from the oranges and separate the flesh into segments.
2. Cut the butter into small pieces, about the size of sugar lumps.
3. Break the chocolate into small pieces and put in a bowl over a pan of gently simmering water, or in the top of a double boiler.
4. Add the coffee and stir until the chocolate has melted. Remove from the heat.
5. Add the butter, egg yolks, icing sugar and orange zest to the chocolate.
6. Return the pan to the heat, and continue stirring until the butter has melted and the ingredients are thoroughly mixed together.
7. Remove from the heat and leave to cool.
8. Beat the egg whites to soft peaks, then fold them half at a time into the chocolate mixture.

9. Pour the mixture into a 450g/1 lb loaf tin lined with cling film. Cover with foil and leave to chill for 1 day.

10. About 30 minutes before serving, dip the loaf tin into a bowl of boiling water for 1 second. Remove the foil and put a plate over the top of the tin. Invert the tin so that the chocolate dessert falls neatly onto the plate. Cut into slices and arrange on a serving dish.

11. Serve garnished with the orange segments and mint leaves.

CHOCOLATE DIP WITH FRUIT

	Fe	Fol	B$_{12}$
	1.2	25	0.03

Serves 4

Metric/Imperial		*American*
115g/4oz	plain chocolate	1/4 lb
2 tbsp	golden syrup	2 tbsp
2 tbsp	smooth peanut butter	2 tbsp
2 tbsp	milk	2 tbsp
1	apple, cored and cut into 8 pieces	1
1	orange, segmented	1
1 small	pineapple, cubed	1 small

1. Break the chocolate into small pieces.
2. Put the chocolate, syrup, peanut butter and milk together in a saucepan. Heat gently, stirring continuously, until the ingredients are blended together.
3. Pour the mixture into a serving bowl. Place on a large plate and arrange the fresh fruit around the edge. Provide skewers for dipping.

DRIED FRUIT SALAD

Serves 4

	Fe	Fol	B$_{12}$
	3.4	35	0

Metric/Imperial		*American*
70g/2½oz	dried pear slices	½ cup
70g/2½oz	dried apple rings	½ cup
70g/2½oz	dried apricots	½ cup
70g/2½oz	stoned dried prunes	½ cup
70g/2½oz	dried figs	½ cup
70g/2½oz	stoned dried dates	½ cup
285ml/½ pint	unsweetened orange juice	1⅓ cups
115g/4oz	flaked almonds	1 cup

1. Put all the fruit in a large bowl.
2. Pour in the orange juice, stir well, then chill for 30 minutes.
3. Serve sprinkled with the almonds.

FRUIT AND ALL-BRAN LOAF

Makes 12 slices

Fe	Fol	B$_{12}$
4.8	56	0.48

Metric/Imperial		*American*
115g/4oz	All-Bran	1^1/2 cups
85g/3oz	caster sugar	^{1}/2 cup
115g/4oz	sultanas	^{2}/3 cup
115g/4oz	seedless raisins	^{2}/3 cup
115g/4oz	dried dates, stoned and chopped	^{2}/3 cup
285ml/^{1}/2 pint	milk	1^1/3 cups
115g/4oz	self-raising brown flour	1 cup

1. Pour the cereal into a large mixing bowl.
2. Add the sugar, sultanas, raisins and dates.
3. Stir in the milk. Mix well, cover and leave for 30 minutes.
4. Sift the flour into the mixture. Tip any remaining bran into the bowl. Mix thoroughly.
5. Pour the cake mixture into a non-stick or lightly greased and lined 900g/2 lb loaf tin.
6. Bake in a preheated oven at 180°C/350°F/gas mark 4 for 1 hour or until cooked.
7. Leave the cake to stand in the tin for 15 minutes, then turn out onto a cooling rack.
8. Slice the cake when cold. Keeps well for up to 1 week if wrapped in foil.

FRUIT BITES

Serves 4

	Fe	Fol	B$_{12}$
	2.1	14	0

Metric/Imperial		*American*
85g/3oz	sultanas	1/2 cup
85g/3oz	currants	1/2 cup
85g/3oz	seedless raisins	1/2 cup
85g/3oz	Brazil nuts	2/3 cup
1 tbsp	freshly squeezed orange juice	1 tbsp

1. Put the dried fruit and two-thirds of the nuts into a liquidizer or food processor. Add the orange juice and process to a smooth paste.
2. Shape the mixture into balls about 2.5cm/1 inch in diameter. Chill for 30 minutes.
3. Chop the remaining nuts. Roll the fruit balls in the chopped nuts to form a coating.
4. Serve in paper cases or on a serving dish.

HERBAL TEA BREAD

Makes 12 slices

	Fe	Fol	B$_{12}$
	2.8	11	0.21

Metric/Imperial		American
55g/2oz	prunes, stoned and chopped	1/3 cup
55g/2oz	dried dates, stoned and chopped	1/3 cup
55g/2oz	dried figs, chopped	1/3 cup
55g/2oz	sultanas	1/3 cup
1	orange, grated zest of	1
1 tsp	dried mixed spice	1 tsp
140ml/1/4 pint	herb tea	2/3 cup
225g/8oz	self-raising flour	2 cups
2 tsp	baking powder	2 tsp
2	eggs, beaten	2
4 tbsp	sunflower oil	4 tbsp

1. Put the dried fruit, orange zest, mixed spice and herb tea into a large mixing bowl. Stir well, cover and leave for 8 hours.
2. Sift the flour and baking powder together. Add to the fruit mixture with the eggs and oil. Mix thoroughly.
3. Pour the mixture into a non-stick or lightly greased and lined 450g/1 lb loaf tin.
4. Bake in a preheated oven at 180°C/350°F/gas mark 4 for 40 minutes. Reduce the heat to 170°C/325°F/gas mark 3 and cook for a further 20 minutes until ready.
5. Leave the tea bread in the tin for 15 minutes, then turn out onto a cooling rack.

Sweet Dishes

6. Cut the loaf when it is thoroughly cooled. Will keep for up to 5 days if wrapped in foil.

Note to Cooks

Can be frozen.

PEANUT BUTTER BISCUITS

Makes 24

Fe	Fol	B$_{12}$
0.3	5	0.05

Metric/Imperial		*American*
85g/3oz	polyunsaturated margarine	1/3 cup
85g/3oz	crunchy peanut butter	1/3 cup
115g/4oz	soft brown sugar	2/3 cup
1	egg, beaten	1
170g/6oz	plain flour	1 1/2 cups
1/2 tsp	bicarbonate of soda	1/2 tsp

1. Put the margarine, peanut butter and sugar in a mixing bowl. Beat for about 10 minutes until the mixture looks light and fluffy.
2. Beat in the egg until well mixed.
3. Sift together the flour and bicarbonate of soda and fold gently into the creamed mixture until evenly distributed. Chill for 1 hour.
4. Shape the mixture into small balls, using your hands. Place the balls spaced well apart on 2 non-stick or lightly greased baking sheets.
5. Make a criss-cross pattern on the top of each ball.
6. Bake in a preheated oven at 190°C/375°F/gas mark 5 for 15 minutes until risen and lightly browned. Cool on a cooling rack.
7. Store in an airtight container for up to 1 week.

PEARS WITH
CHOCOLATE SAUCE

	Fe	Fol	B_{12}
	1.5	6	0

Serves 4

Metric/Imperial		*American*
4 medium	ripe pears	4 medium
140ml/¼ pint	white wine	⅔ cup
140ml/¼ pint	water	⅔ cup
1	cinnamon stick	1

Sauce

285ml/½ pint	water	1⅓ cups
55g/2oz	caster sugar	⅓ cup
1 tsp	cocoa powder	1 tsp
115g/4oz	plain chocolate, broken into pieces	¼ lb

1. Peel the pears being careful to keep them intact with the stalks remaining.
2. Put the pears in a pan and add the wine, water and cinnamon stick. Bring to boiling point.
3. Cover, reduce the heat, and simmer for about 12 minutes or until the pears are tender.
4. To make the sauce, put half the water in a pan and add the sugar, cocoa and chocolate. Stir over a gentle heat until the sauce is smooth. Stir in the remaining water, bring to boiling point, reduce the heat and simmer until the sauce is dark and glossy.
5. Place a pear, standing upright, on the centre of each serving plate. Spoon over the chocolate sauce and serve immediately.

Anaemia

TROPICAL FRUIT SALAD

Serves 4

	Fe	Fol	B$_{12}$
	1.7	41	0

Metric/Imperial		*American*
1 medium	ripe mango	1 medium
2 medium	bananas	2 medium
1 tsp	lemon juice	1 tsp
2 medium	oranges	2 medium
30g/1oz	desiccated coconut	1/3 cup
140ml/1/4 pint	unsweetened orange juice	2/3 cup

1. Peel the mango and place it flat on the work surface. Cut horizontally through the fruit keeping the knife blade in line with the stone. Turn the fruit over and repeat the process. Carefully remove the flesh from the stone and cut into strips.
2. Peel and slice the bananas and brush with the lemon juice.
3. Peel, segment and remove the pips from the oranges.
4. Put the fruit, desiccated coconut and fruit juice in a bowl and gently fold the ingredients together.
5. Chill for 30 minutes before serving.

WHOLEMEAL COOKIES

Makes 24

Fe	Fol	B$_{12}$
0.3	5	0

Metric/Imperial		*American*
140g/5oz	wholemeal flour	1 1/4 cups
1 tsp	baking powder	1 tsp
115g/4oz	polyunsaturated margarine	1/2 cup
55g/2oz	medium oatmeal	1/2 cup
15g/1/2oz	soft brown sugar	1 tbsp
1 tbsp	milk	1 tbsp

1. Sift the flour and baking powder into a mixing bowl. Tip in any bran remaining in the sieve.
2. Add the fat and cut it into the flour until it is in small pieces. Rub in the fat until the mixture resembles fine breadcrumbs.
3. Add the oatmeal, sugar and milk and stir until the mixture holds together.
4. Roll the mixture out thinly on a lightly floured work surface. Cut into rounds using a 5 cm/2 inch cutter. Lightly pierce the surface of the biscuits with a fork.
5. Bake on 2 lightly greased or non-stick baking sheets in a preheated oven at 180°C/350°F/gas mark 4 for 15 minutes or until browned.
6. Leave the biscuits on the baking sheets for 10 minutes, then carefully transfer to a cooling rack.
7. When thoroughly cooled store in an airtight container. Keep for up to 1 week.

Further Reading

Anaemia
Davies, J. *Anaemia*. Thorsons (1993).

Dietary References
Department of Health. *Dietary Reference Values for Food Energy and Nutrients for the United Kingdom*. Report on Health and Social Subjects 41 HMSO (1991).

National Research Council. *Recommended Dietary Allowances* 10th Edition. National Academy Press (1989).

Tables of Food Composition
Davies, J. and Dickerson, J. *Nutrient Content of Food Portions* The Royal Society of Chemistry (1991).

Holland, B., Welch, A.A., Unwin, I.D., Buss, D.H., Paul, A.A. and Southgate, D.A.T. *McCance and Widdowson's The Composition of Foods* 5th extended edition. The Royal Society of Chemistry and Ministry of Agriculture, Fisheries and Food (1991).

Medication
British National Formulary (latest edition). The British Medical Association and the Royal Pharmaceutical Society of Great Britain.

General Index

Recipe Index

Recipe Index